TEACHING
WRITING
STRATEGIES

WORD CHOICES

SENTENCE STRUCTURE

PUNCTUATION

EDITING AND PROOFREADING

DIANE HENDERSON AND BRUCE TUFFIN

Teaching Writing Strategies *(Book 3)*

Published by Prim-Ed Publishing 2018
Copyright© Diane Henderson and Bruce Tuffin 2018

ISBN 978-1-912760-36-7
PR–6808

Titles in this series:
Teaching Writing Strategies *(Book 1)*
Teaching Writing Strategies *(Book 2)*
Teaching Writing Strategies *(Book 3)*
Teaching Writing Strategies *(Book 4)*
Teaching Writing Strategies *(Book 5)*
Teaching Writing Strategies *(Book 6)*

Internet websites
In some cases, websites or specific URLs may be recommended. While these are checked and rechecked at the time of publication, the publisher has no control over any subsequent changes which may be made to webpages. It is *strongly* recommended that the class teacher checks *all* URLs before allowing pupils to access them.

View all pages online

Website: www.prim-ed.com

Email: sales@prim-ed.com

FOREWORD

Teaching Writing Strategies is a series of six books using modelling, guided and independent practice to teach pupils strategies they can use to improve the clarity, correctness and richness of their writing. The focus is on sentences, their structure, punctuation and word choices and on developing editing and proofreading skills and their habitual use.

Titles in this series:
- *Teaching Writing Strategies* (Book 1)
- *Teaching Writing Strategies* (Book 2)
- *Teaching Writing Strategies* (Book 3)
- *Teaching Writing Strategies* (Book 4)
- *Teaching Writing Strategies* (Book 5)
- *Teaching Writing Strategies* (Book 6)

TABLE OF CONTENTS

Teacher Notes .... iv–v
Class Recording Sheets
    Assessment Activities .... vi–ix
    Assessment Writing .... x–xi
Pupil Writing Checklist xii
Pupil Self-evaluation xiii
Curriculum Links .... xiiv–xv

WORD CHOICES

Unit 1   Nouns, Noun Groups and Adjectives 2–7
Unit 2   Pronouns, Using Pronouns, Which Pronoun? 8–13
Unit 3   Verbs and Adverbials 14–19
Unit 4   Verbs: Tense, Matching Verbs 20–25
Assessment 26–29

SENTENCE STRUCTURE

Unit 5   Sentences, Word Order, Questions 30–35
Unit 6   Sentence Beginnings 36–41
Unit 7   Conjunctions 42–47
Unit 8   Paragraphs 48–53
Assessment 54–57

PUNCTUATION

Unit 9   Using Punctuation in Sentences 58–63
Unit 10   Full Stops, Capital Letters, Commas, Direct Speech 64–69
Unit 11   Apostrophes in Contractions 70–75
Unit 12   Apostrophes for Possession 76–81
Assessment 82–85

EDITING AND PROOFREADING

Unit 13   Spelling (Vowel Sounds), Sentence Structure,
            Punctuation, Word Choices, Editing 86–91

Unit 14   Spelling (More Vowel Sounds), Sentence Structure,
            Punctuation, Word Choices, Editing 92–97

Unit 15   Spelling (Suffixes), Sentence Structure,
            Punctuation, Word Choices, Editing 98–103

Unit 16   Spelling (Homophones), Sentence Structure,
            Punctuation, Word Choices, Editing 104–109

Assessment 110–113

TEACHER NOTES

ABOUT WRITING

A good writer is not simply one who knows about and can use text types. A good writer is one with the capacity to produce interesting, informative, grammatically correct text, for a specific purpose, that achieves any writer's intent – clear, precise communication.

TEACHING WRITING

Pupils can and should be taught strategies that will help them to write better. These include improvements in word choices, sentence structure, punctuation and editing and proofreading. Writing strategies taught should be modelled, discussed and then applied, firstly with teacher support and then independently. However, the emphasis should always be on the writing process, which requires forethought, planning and a rational, measured approach in order to produce the desired outcome. Editing and proofreading are essential components of any writing. It is important that pupils edit and proofread habitually, with a specific purpose, and concentrate on the careful consideration of each sentence, one at a time. Activities provided in this series encourage pupils to think about appropriate aspects of their writing before, during and after the process.

LESSON PROCEDURE

Introduction
Discuss the text title with pupils. Ask for their interpretations of what the title could mean.

Discuss the text type. Why does it fit into this category? What are the specific features of this type of text?

Guide the discussion to introduce the teaching points/ strategies to be covered during the course of the unit: for example, check they understand terms such as noun group, adverbial, sentence, paragraph and comma.

Development
Read and discuss the text, either in groups or as a class. Assist pupils with any unfamiliar vocabulary or expressions.

Differentiation
Work through the introductory activities with the class as a whole, ensuring pupils understand what is required of them.

Work with those requiring additional assistance while the remainder of the class work independently on the activities.

Review
In pairs or small groups, pupils review their answers, giving their reasoning where required and critiquing the longer sentence or paragraph responses.

ASSESSMENT

An assessment is included for each unit in the book. Due to the way it is structured, this assessment will allow you to see individual pupil's understandings as well as any common points of weakness which may require further assistance.

FORMAT

Teaching Writing Strategies is organised into four sections:

Word Choices

Sentence Structure

Punctuation

Editing and Proofreading

Each section has four units of work and one assessment unit.

Teaching Units
Each six-page unit of work has a specific focus, two teacher pages and four activity pages.

Assessment Units
- Following each section is a four-page unit of assessment activities – one page for each unit.
- Answers are provided in the teacher pages for that unit.
- Teacher record sheets – see pages vi–ix.

Assessment Writing Tasks
- A suggested paragraph writing topic for each unit is provided on the teacher pages.
- Teacher recording sheets – see pages x–xi.
- Pupil writing checklists – see page xii.
- Pupil self-evaluation – see page xiii.

TEACHER NOTES
Sample Open Pages

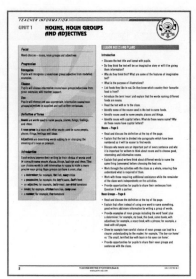

Teacher page 1

Teacher page 2

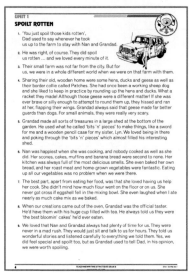

Activity page 1

Activity page 2

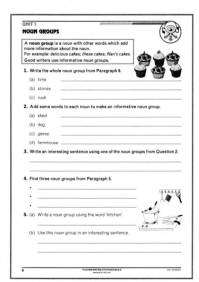

Activity page 3

Activity page 4

ASSESSMENT ACTIVITIES

Date: _____

Name	Unit 1	Unit 2	Unit 3	Unit 4

TEACHING WRITING STRATEGIES (Book 3)
www.prim-ed.com

978-1-912760-36-7

ASSESSMENT ACTIVITIES

Date: _____

Name	Unit 5	Unit 6	Unit 7	Unit 8

ASSESSMENT ACTIVITIES

Date: _____

Name	Unit 9	Unit 10	Unit 11	Unit 12

TEACHING WRITING STRATEGIES (Book 3)
www.prim-ed.com

978-1-912760-36-7

ASSESSMENT ACTIVITIES

Date: _____

Name	Unit 13	Unit 14	Unit 15	Unit 16

ASSESSMENT WRITING

Unit: _____ Focus: _____ Date: _____

Paragraph topic:

Name	Comment

ASSESSMENT WRITING

Unit: _____   Focus: _____   Date: _____

Paragraph topic: _____

Name	Comment

PUPIL WRITING CHECKLIST

Name: _____ Date: _____

Assessment writing topic: _____

Paragraph

I have read the paragraph and it makes sense. .... ☐
I have read it to check for spelling errors. .... ☐
I have made corrections. .... ☐

Punctuation

I have checked the sentences one at a time for:

- *capital letters* to start sentences and proper nouns. .... ☐
- *full stops*, *question marks* and *exclamation marks*. .... ☐
- *commas*. .... ☐
- *apostrophes* for contractions and ownership. .... ☐
- *speech marks*. .... ☐

I have made corrections. .... ☐

Sentences

I have checked the sentences one at a time for:

- *sense* – Does each sentence make sense by itself? .... ☐
- *length* – Are any sentences too long? .... ☐
  - Should they be separated? .... ☐
  - Should some be joined? .... ☐
- *beginnings* – Have I used interesting beginnings? .... ☐
  - I have made changes. .... ☐

Word Choices

verbs – Are they informative and different? .... ☐
  Have I used the correct verb tense? .... ☐
  Are there too many boring verbs? .... ☐
adverbials – Do some verbs need adverbials to tell how,
  when or where something happened? .... ☐
noun groups – Are the noun groups descriptive? .... ☐
  Can I add some descriptive adjectives to tell
  more about nouns and pronouns? .... ☐
pronouns – Have I used the correct pronouns? .... ☐
  I have made changes and corrections. .... ☐

TEACHING WRITING STRATEGIES (Book 3)
www.prim-ed.com

978-1-912760-36-7

PUPIL SELF-EVALUATION

Name: _____ Unit: _____ Date: _____

I wrote a paragraph about: _____

My goal was to focus on: _____

How well did I achieve my goal?   ☆☆☆☆☆

Three things I did well in my writing were:

• _____

• _____

• _____

┌───┐
│ Next time I write a paragraph I will try to: │
│   │
│   │
│   │
│   │
└───┘

PUPIL SELF-EVALUATION

Name: _____ Unit: _____ Date: _____

I wrote a paragraph about: _____

My goal was to focus on: _____

How well did I achieve my goal?   ☆☆☆☆☆

Three things I did well in my writing were:

• _____

• _____

• _____

┌───┐
│ Next time I write a paragraph I will try to: │
│   │
│   │
│   │
│   │
└───┘

CURRICULUM LINKS

ENGLAND

English, Key Stage 2, Year 3

Writing – Transcription
• Use further prefixes and suffixes and understand how to add them.
• Spell further homophones.
• Spell words that are often misspelt.
• Place the possessive apostrophe accurately in words with regular and irregular plurals.

Writing – Composition
• Evaluate and edit by:
• assessing the effectiveness of others' writing and suggesting improvements.
• proposing changes to grammar and vocabulary to improve consistency, including the accurate use of pronouns in sentences.
• Proofread for spelling and punctuation errors.

Writing – Vocabulary, Grammar and Punctuation
• Develop their understanding of the concepts set out in English Appendix 2, by extending the range of sentences with more than one clause by using a wider range of conjunctions; choosing nouns or pronouns appropriately for clarity and cohesion and to avoid repetition; and using conjunctions and adverbs.
• Indicate grammatical and other features by indicating possession by using the possessive apostrophe with plural nouns and using and punctuating direct speech.

NORTHERN IRELAND

Language and Literacy, Key Stage 1, Year 4

Writing
• Begin to check their work in relation to specific criteria.
• Spell correctly a range of familiar, important and regularly occurring words.
• Develop increasing competence in the use of grammar and punctuation.

REPUBLIC OF IRELAND

English Language, 3rd Class

Writing – Developing Competence, Confidence and the Ability to Write Independently
• Develop an awareness of the difference between written language and oral language.
• Learn to revise and re-draft writing.
• Learn to use a wider range of punctuation marks with greater accuracy as part of the revision and editing process.
• Learn to write with increasing grammatical accuracy through the process of revision and editing.

TEACHING WRITING STRATEGIES (Book 3)
www.prim-ed.com

978-1-912760-36-7

CURRICULUM LINKS

SCOTLAND

Literacy and English, Primary 4

Writing – Tools for Writing
• I can spell the most commonly-used words and use resources to help me spell tricky or unfamiliar words.
• I can use appropriate punctuation and order and link sentences in a way that makes sense.
• Throughout the writing process, I can check that my writing makes sense.

WALES

English, Key Stage 2, Year 3

Writing
• Proofread and give an opinion about their own written work and that of others; identify ways to improve and begin to edit.
• Review and improve sections of their work.
• Use language appropriate to writing, including standard forms of English.
• Use nouns, pronouns, adjectives, adverbs, prepositions, connectives and verb tenses in their writing.
• Use adjectives and adverbs to expand simple sentences and phrases.
• Use connectives for causation and consequence.
• Use full stops, question marks, exclamation marks and commas for lists.
• Use past tense of verbs consistently.

UNIT 1 NOUNS, NOUN GROUPS AND ADJECTIVES

Focus

Word choices – nouns, noun groups and adjectives

Progression

Recognise

Pupils will recognise a noun/noun group/adjective from modelled examples.

Choose

Pupils will choose informative nouns/noun groups/adjectives from given examples, with teacher support.

Use

Pupils will choose and use appropriate, informative nouns/noun groups/adjectives in supplied and self-written sentences.

Definition of Terms

Nouns are words used to name people, places, things, feelings and ideas.

A **noun group** is a noun with other words used to name people, places, things, feelings and ideas.

Adjectives are describing words adding to or changing the meaning of a noun or pronoun.

Introduction

Good writers improve their writing by their choice of words used to correctly name people, places, things, feelings and ideas. They can choose words to add information to nouns to make a more precise noun group. Noun groups can have a noun, plus:

- a **determiner**; for example, *the* fish, *many* chips
- a **possessive**; for example, the *boy's* pasta, *Dad's* food
- an **adjective**; for example, *tasty* meal, *sun-dried* tomatoes
- **nouns**; for example, *kitchen* benches, *camp* oven
- a **number**; for example, *five* tomatoes

Introduction

- Discuss the text title and layout with pupils.
- Do they think the text will be an imaginative story or will it be giving them information?
- Why do they think this? What are some of the features of imaginative text?
- What is the purpose of illustrations?
- List foods they like to eat. Do they know which country their favourite food is from?
- Introduce the term 'noun' and explain that the words naming different foods are nouns.
- Read the text with or to the class.
- Identify some of the nouns used in the text to name foods.
- Identify nouns used to name people, places and things.
- Identify nouns with capital letters. What do these nouns name? Why do these nouns have capital letters?

Nouns – Page 5

- Read and discuss the definition at the top of the page.
- Explain that the text is divided into paragraphs which have been numbered so it will be easier to find words.
- Discuss why nouns are an important part of every sentence and why it is important for writers to think about nouns and to choose good, interesting and informative nouns.
- Explain that good writers think about different words to name the same thing (synonyms) before choosing the best one.
- Work through the activities with the class as a whole, ensuring they understand what is required of them.
- Work with those requiring additional assistance while the remainder of the class work independently on the activities.
- Provide opportunities for pupils to share their sentences from Question 3 with a partner.

Noun Groups – Page 6

- Read and discuss the definition at the top of the page.
- Explain that often instead of using one word to name something, good writers add more information by writing a group of words.
- Provide examples of noun groups including the word 'book' plus a determiner; for example, *my book*, *this book*, *some books*, with adjectives; for example, *a scary book*, with a phrase; for example, *a book with old pages*.
- Show by example how careful choice of noun groups can lead to a clearer understanding by the reader; for example, 'The boy ran home' vs 'The small, terrified boy with tears in his eyes ran home'.
- Provide opportunities for pupils to share their noun groups and sentences with the class.

UNIT 1 — NOUNS, NOUN GROUPS AND ADJECTIVES

Adjectives – Page 7

- Read and discuss the definition at the top of the page.
- Brainstorm adjectives to describe a person using their sense of sight, smell, hearing and touch and their feelings. This will assist them to complete Question 5.
- Provide opportunities to share their answers to Question 5.

ANSWERS

Nouns – Page 5

1. (a) racket
   (b) guards
   (c) geese

2. (a) flour
   (b) sword
   (c) vegetables
   (d) treasures

3. Teacher check

4. scones, cakes, muffins, banana bread, bread, vegetables, meat

Noun Groups – Page 6

1. (a) plenty of time
   (b) wonderful stories
   (c) mad rush

2.–3. Teacher check

4. Answers may include: a large shed, a wooden pencil case, his interesting shed.

5. Teacher check

Adjectives – Page 7

1. Teacher check

2. (a) far better
   (b) working sheep
   (c) old, wooden

3.–5. Teacher check

Assessment Activity – Page 26

1. (a) vegetables
   (b) treasure
   (c) flour
   (d) racket

2. Teacher check

3. an old farmhouse with a beautiful garden

4.–6. Teacher check

Class Record Sheet – Page vi

ASSESSMENT WRITING

- **Paragraph Topic** – *Yummy Food*
- **Focus: Word Choices** – *nouns, noun groups and adjectives*

Self-evaluation – Page xiii

SPOILT ROTTEN

1. 'You just spoil those kids rotten',
   Dad used to say whenever he took
   us up to the farm to stay with Nan and Grandad.

2. He was right, of course. They did spoil
   us rotten … and we loved every minute of it.

3. Their small farm was not far from the city. But for
   us, we were in a whole different world when we were on that farm with them.

4. Sharing their old, wooden home were some hens, ducks and geese as well as
   their border collie called Patches. She had once been a working sheep dog
   and she liked to keep in practice by rounding up the hens and ducks. What a
   racket they made! Although those geese were a different matter! If she was
   ever brave or silly enough to attempt to round them up, they hissed and ran
   at her, flapping their wings. Grandad always said that geese made far better
   guards than dogs. For small animals, they were really very scary.

5. Grandad made all sorts of treasures in a large shed at the bottom of the
   garden. He used what he called 'bits 'n' pieces' to make things, like a sword
   for me and a wooden pencil case for my sister, Lyn. We loved being in there
   and poking through the 'bits 'n' pieces' which almost filled his interesting
   shed.

6. Nan was happiest when she was cooking, and nobody cooked as well as she
   did. Her scones, cakes, muffins and banana bread were second to none. Her
   kitchen was always full of the most delicious smells. She even baked her own
   bread, and her roast meat and home-grown vegetables were fantastic. Eating
   up all our vegetables was no problem when we were there.

7. The best part, apart from eating her food, was that she loved having us help
   her cook. She didn't mind how much flour went on the floor or on us. She
   never got cross if eggshell fell in the mixing bowl. She even laughed when I ate
   nearly as much cake mix as we baked.

8. When our creations came out of the oven, Grandad was the official taster.
   He'd have them with his huge cup filled with tea. He always told us they were
   'the best bloomin' cakes' he'd ever eaten.

9. We loved that Nan and Grandad always had plenty of time for us. They were
   never in a mad rush. They would just sit and talk to us for hours. They told us
   wonderful stories and listened carefully to everything we told them. Yes, we
   did feel special and spoilt too, but as Grandad used to tell Dad, in his opinion,
   we were worth spoiling.

TEACHING WRITING STRATEGIES (Book 3)
www.prim-ed.com

978-1-912760-36-7

Nouns are naming words for people, places and things. For example: *Nan*, *farm*, *scones*. Good writers choose their naming words or nouns carefully.

1. Which noun in Paragraph 4 means:

(a) a loud noise? _____

(b) people who protect a property? _____

(c) the plural of goose? _____

2. Choose the best noun for each sentence.

treasures   *flour*   *vegetables*   *sword*

(a) We often spilt _____ all over the floor.

(b) I pretended I was a soldier fighting with my _____.

(c) Grandad grew many different _____ in his garden.

(d) Grandad's _____ were kept in his shed.

3. Write an interesting sentence for each noun.

(a) flour _____

_____

(b) oven _____

_____

(c) cakes _____

_____

(d) bits 'n' pieces _____

_____

_____

4. Write a list of nouns naming things that Nan cooked.

_____

NOUN GROUPS

> A **noun group** is a noun with other words which add more information about the noun.
> For example: *delicious cakes; these cakes; Nan's cakes.*
> Good writers use informative noun groups.

1. Write the whole noun group from Paragraph 9.

   (a) time _____

   (b) stories _____

   (c) rush _____

2. Add some words to each noun to make an informative noun group.

   (a) shed _____

   (b) dog _____

   (c) geese _____

   (d) farmhouse _____

3. Write an interesting sentence using one of the noun groups from Question 2.

_____

_____

4. Find three noun groups from Paragraph 5.

   • _____

   • _____

   • _____

5. (a) Write a noun group using the word 'kitchen'.

   _____

   (b) Use this noun group in an interesting sentence.

_____

_____

TEACHING WRITING STRATEGIES (Book 3)
www.prim-ed.com
978-1-912760-36-7

> **Adjectives** are describing words. They can tell more about a noun. For example, a *delicious*, *tasty* dish.

1. Choose some interesting adjectives you could use to describe each noun.

    (a) muffins _____

    (b) cup _____

    (c) sword _____

2. Write the adjectives used in Paragraph 4 to describe each noun.

    (a) _____ guards

    (b) _____ dog

    (c) _____ home

3. Use each adjective to describe a noun in an interesting sentence.

    (a) fantastic _____

    _____

    (b) horrible _____

    _____

4. Add adjectives to make the sentences more descriptive.

    (a) The _____ girl cooked some _____ pasta.

    (b) A _____ chef made a _____ sandwich.

5. Write a paragraph about your favourite food on the back of this page. Before you start, think about adjectives you could use to tell how it looks, tastes, smells, sounds and feels. Write these adjectives in the box.

UNIT 2   PRONOUNS, USING PRONOUNS, WHICH PRONOUN?

Focus

Word choices – pronouns, using pronouns, which pronouns?

Progression

Recognise

Pupils will recognise a pronoun from modelled examples.

Choose

Pupils will choose appropriate pronouns from given examples, with teacher support.

Use

Pupils will choose and use correct and appropriate pronouns in supplied and self-written sentences.

Definition of Terms

Pronouns are words used to replace nouns.

Personal pronouns are used in place of a person or thing.

A **relative pronoun** comes before the clause describing the noun or pronoun to which it refers.

A **possessive pronoun** replaces a noun identifying ownership by the person or thing to which it refers.

The **subject** of a verb is the person or thing 'doing' the action.

The **object** of a verb is the person or thing affected by the action.

Introduction

Good writers improve their writing by replacing nouns with appropriate and correct pronouns. The use of pronouns prevents constant repetition of a noun, making text more manageable and fluid. It is important for pupils to know the correct pronouns to use in the context of a sentence.

Possessive pronouns are used to replace the name of a person or thing; for example, *That bag belongs to **him** (Dad), it is **his***.

Note: The words 'his' and 'its' can be used as a possessive determiner as well as a possessive pronoun; for example, his bag, its tail.

The following table shows subjective, objective and possessive personal pronouns.

Note: Subjective and objective pronouns are required when the pronoun refers to the subject or object of the verb; for example, I (subject) *boarded the ship. The crew welcomed us* (object) *onboard.*

Personal Pronouns

Person	Subjective	Objective	Emphatic/ reflexive	Possessive
First singular	I	me	myself	mine
Second	you	you	yourself	yours
Third (male)	he	him	himself	his
Third (female)	she	her	herself	hers
Third (neuter)	it	it	itself	its
First plural	we	us	ourselves	ours
Second	you	you	yourselves	yours
Third	they	them	themselves	theirs

The **relative pronouns** 'who', 'which' and 'that' are used to refer to nouns and pronouns; for example, the boy who, he who, the team that, the book which.

The correct use of 'who' for people is more critical. Although 'which' and 'that' can both be used in many contexts, 'which' should strictly be used to refer to a particular desk (telling which one); for example, *the desk which is by the door*. The relative pronoun 'that' has a broader reference and doesn't refer to one desk; for example, *the desks that are by the door.*

LESSON NOTES AND PLANS

Introduction

- Discuss the text title with pupils.
- Do they think the text will be an imaginative story or will it be giving them information?
- Why do they think this? What are some of the features of informative and imaginative text?
- Introduce the term 'pronoun' and explain that words replacing nouns are pronouns. Use examples from the classroom; for example, Paul = he, Mary = she, the board = it, the tallest boy in the class = he.
- Read the text with or to the class.
- Identify some of the pronouns used in the text to replace people, places and things.
- Identify single and plural pronouns from the text.

Pronouns – Page 11

- Read and discuss the definition at the top of the page.
- Explain that good writers use pronouns instead of repeating the same nouns.
- Explain why it is important to use the correct pronoun for the noun it replaces.
- Work through the activities with the class as a whole, ensuring they understand what is required of them.
- Work with those requiring additional assistance while the remainder of the class work independently on the activities.

UNIT 2   PRONOUNS, USING PRONOUNS, WHICH PRONOUN?

Using Pronouns – Page 12

• Discuss the text at the top of the page.

• Provide opportunities for the class to share their answers to Question 2.

Which Pronoun – Who or That? Me or I? – Page 13

• Questions 1 and 2 focus on the relative pronouns 'who' and 'that'.

• Explain that 'who' must be used for people. NOTE: 'That' and 'which' refer to things, places and can both be used for groups of people; for example, the team *which*, a class *that*, (but 'the members of the team *who*').

• Encourage pupils to read the sentences in Question 3 aloud to help them to choose the correct pronouns. Encourage them to ask the question 'Who did it?'; if the answer is 'I', then 'I' is correct; if not, it should be 'me'.

• Explain that in Question 4 they will be doing something that many adults find difficult, but if they use the hint it will be easier. Many adults believe that they should always say; for example, 'My brother and I' when 'My brother and me' is often correct.

ANSWERS

Pronouns – Page 11

1. (a) He
   (b) They
   (c) They
   (d) it

2. (a) he
   (b) it
   (c) it
   (d) I

3. (a) him
   (b) her
   (c) us
   (d) them
   (e) me

4 (a) I
   (b) he
   (c) they
   (d) You
   (e) it

Using Pronouns – Page 12

1. (a) The nouns are repeated and not replaced by pronouns.
   (b) The boy was at the shops when he heard a man talking to him. The man asked him if he could read a sign. It was on the wall. The boy said he could read it. So he read it to the man in a loud, clear voice.

2. Teacher check

Which Pronoun – Who or That? Me or I? – Page 13

1. (a) ✗
   (b) ✓
   (c) ✗

2. who, that, who

3. (a) me
   (b) I, me
   (c) me, I

4. (a) ✓
   (b) ✗
   (c) ✓
   (d) ✗
   (e) ✗

ASSESSMENT ANSWERS

Assessment Activity – Page 27

1. (a) it
   (b) they
   (c) she

2. (a) we
   (b) I
   (c) he

3. (a) yours
   (b) theirs
   (c) mine

4. (a) that
   (b) who

5. The first time I rode a horse was on a farm. It was only small and it behaved. The teacher led me around. She/He told me I was holding the reins too tightly and I had to let go of them a bit.

Class Record Sheet – Page vi

ASSESSMENT WRITING

• **Paragraph Topic** – *Skateboarding*

• **Focus: Word Choices** – *pronouns, using pronouns, which pronouns?*

Self-evaluation – Page xiii

WHO ME?

1. 'Hey kid', called the man standing near the entrance. I looked up for a second, thinking that he couldn't be talking to me. I'd never seen him before in my life.

2. It was the school holidays and I was at the local shops by myself for the first time. My friends were all busy or had gone away somewhere with their families. But I didn't care, I was feeling good and having a great time there by myself.

3. Then I heard him say it again. This time when I looked up I could see that he was pointing his finger at me.

4. 'Yes', I mumbled. 'Are you talking to me? Do you want me for something?'

5. 'That's right', he answered. 'Can you read?'

6. 'Of course I can', I replied. I'm actually a very good reader, but I couldn't see what that had to do with him. What a weird question!

7. 'Can you read that sign over there?' He was pointing to a large sign attached to the wall.

8. 'Of course', I answered, thinking there must be something wrong with this man. He looked okay, he was well-dressed and he spoke in a quiet, polite voice.

9. I knew I wasn't supposed to talk to strangers. We'd certainly had that hammered into our heads constantly at school and at home, too. I thought about it for a moment, but I didn't feel I was in any kind of stranger-danger situation. There were lots of other people around and he was some distance away from me, so I wasn't worried about talking to him. I wondered if he had a problem with his eyes or something.

10. 'What's it say then?' he asked in a mildly interested kind of way.

11. 'It says, "No skateboarding allowed"', I read in a loud, clear voice.

12. 'Are you sure?' he asked. His eyes were firmly fixed on my skateboard.

13. I just jumped off, picked it up and went home. I didn't feel all that smart.

TEACHING WRITING STRATEGIES (Book 3)
www.prim-ed.com
978-1-912760-36-7

PRONOUNS

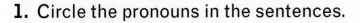

> A pronoun is used to replace a noun.
> For example: 'the people' – *they*; 'a skateboard' – *it.*

1. Circle the pronouns in the sentences.

   (a) The man called out. He wanted to talk to the boy.

   (b) Some of his friends were not there. They were away.

   (c) The boy went to the shops. They were close to home.

   (d) The man said, 'Hey kid'. Then the boy heard the man say it again.

2. Circle the correct pronoun.

   (a) The man was a stranger but | *he* | *she* | *they* | wasn't a danger.

   (b) He was on his skateboard, then he picked | *them* | *it* | *he* | up.

   (c) The man looked at the sign and asked what | *they* | *them* | *it* | said.

   (d) The man pointed to the sign and asked if | *I* | *me* | *we* | could read it.

3. Choose pronouns to write in each space.

him   her   me   us   them

   (a) Please tell that boy I would like to speak to _____.

   (b) I told Sarah I would go skating with _____.

   (c) We are going shopping, so please come with _____.

   (d) I've lost my keys, please help me find _____.

   (e) I'll look in the car park if you will come with _____.

4. Write a correct pronoun in the space.

   (a) Sarah is my friend and _____ want to go skating with her.

   (b) The man is well-dressed and _____ speaks politely.

   (c) Don't tell Mum and Dad because _____ will growl at me.

   (d) _____ are my best friend.

   (e) I can't find my skateboard. Do you know where _____ is?

 **NO SKATEBOARDING**

The boy was at the shops when **the boy** heard a man talking to **the boy**. The man asked **the boy** if **the boy** could read a sign. **The sign** was on the wall. The boy said **the boy** could read **the sign**. So **the boy** read **the sign** to the man in a loud, clear voice.

1. Read the text.

   (a) What is the problem? _____

   _____

   (b) Change all the highlighted nouns to pronouns and write the new text.

   _____

   _____

   _____

   _____

   _____

2. Write interesting sentences using the pronouns.

   (a) hers _____

   _____

   (b) you _____

   _____

   (c) him _____

   _____

   (d) them _____

   _____

   (e) mine _____

   _____

WHICH PRONOUN – WHO OR THAT? ME OR I?

Good writers use the pronoun 'who' for people and 'that' for other things. For example: the man **who ...**, the shops **that ...**

1. Which sentences have the correct pronouns? Put a tick or a cross in the boxes.

(a) The children that I saw at the park go to my school. ☐

(b) There was a group of boys who were bullying a small boy. ☐

(c) The people that visit West Park really enjoy it. ☐

2. Add 'who' or 'that'.

The boys in my class _____ did well in the tests _____ we all

had to do last week were the ones _____ always listen to our teacher.

Good writers use **me** or **I** correctly. They use **I** when I am the person doing something. *I am reading.* So **I** is the subject of the verb.
They use **me** when I am NOT the person doing something. *Mum is reading to **me**.* So, **me** is the object of the verb.

3. Write 'I' or 'me' in the space.

(a) The man gave _____ some advice.

(b) _____ didn't think he was talking to _____.

(c) He told _____ that _____ should read the sign.

When **I** and **me** are used with other people, it's harder to know which one to use. HINT: Try saying the sentence with only the pronoun.
Example 1: My brother and (I or me) went sailing.
    Is it – **I** went sailing, or **me** went sailing?
Example 2: It belongs to my brother and (I or me).
    Is it – It belongs to **me,** or it belongs to **I**?

4. Are the pronouns correct? Put a tick or cross in the boxes.

(a) Then my sister and I went down to the river to go sailing. ☐

(b) Mum said she and me could take a picnic to share. ☐

(c) Dad said he and I would go sailing first. ☐

(d) He thought this might cause a fight between Sam and I. ☐

(e) In the end, Sam and me had fun sailing together. ☐

UNIT 3   VERBS AND ADVERBIALS

978-1-912760-36-7

Focus

Word choices – verbs and adverbials

Progression

Recognise

Pupils will recognise a verb or adverbial from modelled examples.

Choose

Pupils will choose the more or most informative verb or adverbial from given examples, with teacher support.

Use

Pupils will choose and use appropriate, informative verbs or adverbials in supplied and self-written sentences.

Definition of Terms

Verbs or 'doing' words show actions or states of being or having.

Adverbials are words or groups of words that add information, usually to a verb or verb group. They can tell how (manner), when (time) or where (place) something happens. Adverbs can modify (add information to) any words that are not nouns or pronouns. (These are modified by adjectives.)

Paragraphs are sections of writing dealing with a particular subject or point, beginning on a new line.

Persuasive texts are written to put forward a position which the writer wishes to persuade others to share.

Introduction

Good writers improve their writing by their choice of informative and appropriate verbs and adverbials.

LESSON NOTES AND PLANS

Introduction

- Discuss the text title with pupils.
- What do they know about water?
- List things water can do.
- Introduce the term 'verbs' and explain that the words telling what water can do are verbs.
- Read the text with or to the class.
- Ask pupils to identify the text type and discuss the features of a poem.
- Identify some of the action verbs used in the text.

Verbs – Page 17

- Read and discuss the definition at the top of the page.
- Discuss why verbs are important part of every sentence and why it is important for writers to think about verbs and choose good, interesting and informative verbs.
- Work through the activities with the class as a whole, ensuring they understand what is required of them.
- Work with those requiring additional assistance while the remainder of the class work independently on the activities.

Boring Verbs – Page 18

- Review pupils' understanding of the term 'verb' and ask them to provide examples.
- Discuss the over-use of boring verbs like *saw*, *went* and *said* and give alternatives for said, such as *yelled*, *screamed* and *whispered*.
- Explain that better verbs can give more information about what is happening and can change the meaning of a sentence.
- Brainstorm and list more informative verbs for 'got'. This will assist pupils to complete Questions 2 and 3.

Adverbials – Page 19

- Read and discuss the definition of adverbials and the examples given.
- Explain that good writers add adverbials to give the reader more information about verbs and to make their writing more interesting.
- Brainstorm and make three lists of adverbials that could tell *how*, *when* and *where*.
- In pairs or small groups, pupils review their answers for Questions 2–6.

UNIT 3   VERBS AND ADVERBIALS

ANSWERS

Verbs – Page 17

1. (a) pound
(b) wander
(c) sparkle

2. (a) tumble, gush, rush, flow
(b) pound, hammer, approach, arrive
(c) Teacher check

3. (a) Teacher check
(b) Answers may include: flow, tumbled, rush

4. Teacher check

Boring Verbs – Page 18

1. (a)–(b) Teacher check
(c) Answers may include–walked, ran, travelled, drove, cycled, flew, skipped

2. (a)–(c) Teacher check
(d) Answers may include–earned, received, bought, caught, obtained, found, grabbed

3.–4. Teacher check

Adverbials – Page 19

1. (a) restlessly
(b) in the country
(c) at sunrise

2. (a) when
(b) where
(c) how

3.–6. Teacher check

ASSESSMENT ANSWERS

Assessment Activity – Page 28

1. (a) tumbled
(b) hammer
(c) sparkling

2.–5. Teacher check

Class Record Sheet – Page vi

ASSESSMENT WRITING

• **Paragraph Topic** – *Water*
• **Focus: Word Choices** – *pronouns*

Self-evaluation – Page viii

I LOVE WATER

1. I love waterfalls
   that tumble and gush
   making misty rainbows
   as they restlessly rush
   their waters flow and flow.

2. I love rivers
   that wander and go
   through city and field
   so stately and slow
   their secrets tightly sealed.

3. I love the sea
   urgent waves that pound
   and hammer the shore
   approaching with no sound
   to arrive there with a roar.

4. I love cool lakes
   waters deep and blue
   sparkling in the sun
   a twinkling, shining view
   their flowing now is done.

5. I love my bath
   my soap-bubbled sea
   just me there all alone
   so warm and carefree
   in this sea I call my own.

A **verb** is a doing word. For example: We **read** books. The water **runs**. Good writers choose their action **verbs** carefully. For example: Instead of writing, 'The water **ran**.', a better writer could write, 'The water **tumbled** and **gushed**.'.

---

1. Choose the best verb for each sentence.

pound   *sparkle*   *wander*

(a) The huge waves _____ across the shore.

(b) Rivers _____ through the countryside.

(c) The bright sun will _____ on the lakes.

2. Read the poem again.

(a) In the first verse, circle the verbs that can tell how waterfalls move.

(b) In the third verse, circle the verbs that can tell what the sea does.

(c) Use one of these verbs to write an interesting sentence about water.

_____

_____

3. Read the verbs from Verse 2.

love   *wander*   *go*   *sealed*

(a) Write an interesting sentence using one of the verbs.

_____

_____

(b) Write two other verbs for 'go'. _____ _____

4. (a) Write an interesting verb from Verse 1. _____

(b) Write a sentence using this verb.

_____

_____

BORING VERBS

> We use some verbs like *went* too often. A better verb would tell how something went.

1. Write each sentence using a better verb.

(a) The river <u>went</u> to the open sea.

_____

(b) The waterfall <u>went</u> down the mountain.

_____

(c) Write three more interesting verbs for '<u>went</u>'.

_____   _____   _____

2. Write a better word for 'got' in each sentence.

(a) Last night, I <u>got</u> into my bath.   _____

(b) The waves <u>got</u> to the shore.   _____

(c) They <u>got</u> out of the bus.   _____

(d) Write three more interesting verbs for 'got'.

_____   _____   _____

3. Think of an interesting sentence using the verb 'got'. Write this sentence using a better, more descriptive verb.

_____

_____

4. Write two sentences about watching waterfalls.
You must not use the verb 'saw'.

• _____

_____

• _____

_____

TEACHING WRITING STRATEGIES (Book 3)
www.prim-ed.com
978-1-912760-36-7

ADVERBIALS

An **adverbial** can tell when, how or where the verb happens. For example: *Today,* (when) the water flowed *quickly* (how) *into the lake* (where).

1. Circle the adverbial in each sentence telling more about the verb.

(a) The waterfalls restlessly <u>rush</u>.

(b) Some rivers <u>flow</u> in the country.

(c) The lake <u>sparkles</u> at sunrise.

2. Circle the adverbial for each verb.
Write 'how', 'when' or 'where' on the line.

(a) I <u>love</u> my bath at night. _____

(b) Rivers <u>flow</u> through city and field. _____

(c) The sea <u>approaches</u> with no sound. _____

3. Add an adverbial to tell 'how'.

(a) The waves pound _____

(b) Rivers wander _____

4. Add an adverbial to tell 'when'.

(a) The waves pound _____

(b) Rivers wander _____

5. Add an adverbial to tell 'where'.

(a) The waves pound _____

(b) Rivers wander _____

6. (a) Write a sentence about **how** something rushed. Make it interesting.

_____

_____

(b) Write the adverbial from your sentence. _____

UNIT 4   VERBS: TENSE, MATCHING VERBS

Focus

Word choices – choosing correct verbs: tense, consistency, subject, regular irregular

Progression

Recognise
Pupils will recognise the tense of a verb; subject–verb agreement (asking 'who or what is doing the action?'); regular and irregular verbs; and auxiliary verbs, from modelled examples.

Choose
Pupils will choose the tense of a verb; subject–verb agreement; regular and irregular verbs; and auxiliary verbs, from given examples, with teacher support.

Use
Pupils will use the correct tense; subject–verb agreement; regular and irregular verbs; and auxiliary verbs in self-written sentences and paragraphs.

Definition of Terms

Verbs or 'doing' words show actions or states of being or having.

Subject–verb agreement – The form of the verb must match who or what is Performing the action; for example, *I am reading. They are reading.* The *main verb* is the verb describing the action.

Auxiliary verbs are verbs added to the main verb which can change its tense; for example, *He swims. He is swimming. He had been swimming.*

Regular verbs follow regular pattern when changing from the present to the past tense; for example, shop – shopped, rate – rated.

Irregular verbs are verbs which do not follow a regular pattern when changing from the present to the past tense; for example, buy – bought, swim – swam, fly – flew.

Auxiliary verbs
The verbs 'to be' and 'to have' are used as auxiliary or 'helper' verbs. They have many forms which change with the subject and the tense. See the chart below.

Person	Pronoun	The verb 'to be' Present	The verb 'to be' Past	The verb 'to have' Present	The verb 'to have' Past
First (singular)	I	am	was	have	had
Second	you	are	were	have	had
Third	he/she/it	is	was	has	had
First (plural)	we	are	were	have	had
Second	you	are	were	have	had
Third	they	are	were	have	had

Introduction

Good writers improve their writing by their choice and use of correct verb forms for emphasis and to make meaning explicit.

Introduction

- Discuss the text title with pupils.
- What do they think the text may be about?
- Ask pupils to identify the text type.
- Revise the term 'verbs' and list some examples of what people do (verbs).
- Read the text to or with the class.
- Identify some of the action verbs used in the text.

Verb Tense – Page 23

- Read and discuss the definition at the top of the page.
- Discuss why verbs are an important part of every sentence and why it is important for writers to use the correct verb tense.
- Discuss and elicit from pupils the tense of the story (past tense – it has happened).
- Work through the activities with the class as a whole, ensuring they understand what is required of them.
- Work with those requiring additional assistance while the remainder of the class work independently on the activities.

Past Tense Verbs – Page 24

- Review pupils' understanding of the term 'verb' and ask them to provide examples.
- Discuss changing verbs to past tense. Most add 'd' or 'ed'.
- Ask pupils to list some common irregular past tenses; for example, catch – caught, say – said.

Matching Verbs – Page 25

- Discuss with pupils how verb forms change, depending on who or what is doing the action. Use simple examples; *I am running; we are running.*
- Introduce the concept of the subject; i.e. ask who or what is doing the action; for example, *The Islanders are catching fish.* Ask 'who or what' are catching fish. The Islanders (subject) are catching.
- Work through the activities with the class as a whole, ensuring they understand what is required of them.
- Provide opportunities to share and discuss sentences from Question 4 with a partner.

978-1-912760-36-7

UNIT 4   VERBS: TENSE, MATCHING VERBS

ANSWERS

Verb Tense – Page 23

1. (a) live (present)
   (b) will want (future)
   (c) grew (past)

2. Teacher check

3. (a) was
   (b) took
   (c) were
   (d) is

Past Tense Verbs – Page 24

1. Teacher check

2. (a) left
   (b) made
   (c) sold

3.–4. Teacher check

Matching Verbs – Page 25

1. (a) were bombed (the islands)
   (b) stay (the people on West Island)
   (c) had ended (the copra industry)

2. (a) ✓
   (b) ✗
   (c) ✗
   (d) ✗

3.–5. Teacher check

ASSESSMENT ANSWERS

Assessment Activity – Page 29

1. (a) will visit (future)
   (b) sold (past)
   (c) is (present)

2. (a) was
   (b) were sent
   (c) came

3. (a) enjoyed
   (b) came
   (c) swam

4. Teacher check

5. (a) landed (the visitors)
   (b) go (the teachers)
   (c) could be seen (Huge crabs)

6. (a) ✗
   (b) ✓
   (c) ✗
   (d) ✓
   (e) ✗

Class Record Sheet – Page vi

ASSESSMENT WRITING

- **Paragraph Topic** – *My Favourite Island*
- **Focus: Word Choices** – *verbs: tense, matching verbs*

Self-evaluation – Page xiii

THE COCOS ISLANDS

1. The Cocos Keeling Islands are limestone and coral islands in the Indian Ocean off the west coast of Australia. These remote islands are too small to appear on maps. They are 2,768 km from Perth in Australia and about 1,000 km from Java in Indonesia.

Early History

2. In the early 1800s, the valuable coconut palms growing there attracted British and Dutch people who established settlements on some of the larger islands. A number of settlements were established on some of the larger islands. Workers, mainly from Indonesia and Malaysia, and convicts were used as slaves, collecting and breaking open the coconuts.

3. Cocos was so far from any other country that they made up their own laws and had their own money. Distance also made it almost impossible for workers to leave these islands.

4. Food was always a problem and their diet was not very healthy.

The 20th Century

5. In 1901, a cable station was set up on Direction Island with a staff of 40 people. This underwater communication cable linked Australia, South Africa and Singapore.

6. During World War II, the islands were bombed many times. The military base and airstrip there made them an enemy target. At this time, the population of almost 1,500 people relied on shipping for most of their supplies, even for rice. When ships didn't come, they were forced to survive on fish and coconuts.

7. In 1955, Australia took over responsibility for the islands from the British.

8. The Clunies Ross family, who had been involved with the Cocos Islands since those very early times, sold the islands to Australia in 1978.

9. By 1987, the copra industry had ended and many Cocos Malays left the islands.

Today

10. The largest island in this group of islands is West Island. The people who live on West Island are mostly Australians. They usually work there for about two years.

11. The other inhabited island is Home Island. It is the Cocos Malays' permanent home.

12. The beautiful, white sandy beaches of Direction Island attract many yachts which anchor there, but not in summer, which is the cyclone season.

13. Regular flights now make it possible for a limited number of tourists to visit these islands to enjoy great fishing, snorkelling and diving.

VERB TENSE

> **Verbs** can tell us about what has happened in the *past*,
> what is happening now in the *present* and what will happen in the *future*.
> • Their diet *was* not very healthy. (*past*)
> • The sandy beaches *attract* many yachts. (*present*)
> • Regular flights *will make* it possible to visit. (*future*)

1. Underline the verbs. Write 'past', 'present' or 'future' after each sentence.

    (a) Mostly Australians live on West Island. _____

    (b) People will want to visit the Cocos Islands. _____

    (c) Coconut palms grew all over the islands. _____

> There are some smaller verbs that help with tense.
> *will* = future tense   *is/are* = present tense   *had/was/were* = past tense

2. Write an interesting sentence about something you:

    (a) are looking at now. _____

    _____

    _____

    (b) looked at yesterday. _____

    _____

    _____

    (c) will do tomorrow. _____

    _____

    _____

3. Correct the tense of the verb and write it on the line.

    (a) A cable station is set up in 1901. _____

    (b) In 1955, Australia takes over responsibility. _____

    (c) During World War II, the islands are bombed many times. _____

    (d) The largest island will be called West Island. _____

PAST TENSE VERBS

> Changing most verbs to the past tense is easy – we add 'ed' or 'd'.
> For example: live – *lived*, collect – *collected*.

1. Write a short, interesting sentence using the past tense of each regular verb.

   (a) use _____

   _____

   (b) involve _____

   _____

   (c) survive _____

   _____

> Some past tense verbs need to change more. For example: come – *came*,
> break – *broke.*

2. Write the past tense of each verb on the line.

   (a) Many Cocos Malays leave the islands. _____

   (b) Cocos Islanders make up their own laws. _____

   (c) The Clunies Ross family sell the islands to Australia. _____

> Past tense verbs like *seen* and *done*
> always need a helper like *has* and *was*.

3. Write each verb with a helper.

   (a) seen _____   (b) done _____

   (c) gone _____   (d) been _____

4. (a) Write a sentence using 'seen' and its helper.

   _____

   _____

   (b) Write a sentence using 'done' and its helper.

   _____

   _____

MATCHING VERBS

> Verbs change to show who or what is doing the action.
> For example: I *am*, You *are*, He *is*, They *are*.

1. Circle the verb then draw a line under who or what is doing the action.

   (a) The islands were bombed many times.

   (b) The people on West Island usually only stay about two years.

   (c) By 1987, the copra industry had ended.

2. Put a tick or a cross after each sentence to show if the verb group is correct.

   (a) The people ***were eating*** fish and coconuts. ☐

   (b) The coconut palms ***attracts*** British and Dutch people. ☐

   (c) Yachtsmen ***do*** not ***visits*** in summer because of cyclones. ☐

   (d) Home Island ***are inhabited*** by Cocos Malays. ☐

3. Write a verb or verb group to match who or what is doing the action.

   (a) On the larger islands, a number of settlements _____.

   (b) The Clunies Ross family _____ the Cocos Islands.

   (c) Workers _____ as slaves.

   (d) With regular flights, tourists _____ these islands.

4. Write an interesting sentence about an island. Choose your verbs carefully.

   _____

   _____

5. What do you think about the Cocos Islands? Think carefully about the verbs you use.

   _____

   _____

   _____

NOUNS, NOUN GROUPS AND ADJECTIVES

Name: _____ Date: _____

1. Choose the best noun for each sentence.

treasure   *flour*   *vegetables*   *racket*

(a) The _____ grown at home always taste better.

(b) They found some _____ stored in the old shed.

(c) Add the _____ to the butter to make a cake.

(d) Stop making all that _____, I'm trying to sleep.

2. Write an interesting sentence using each noun.

(a) banana bread _____

_____

(b) cupcakes _____

_____

3. Circle the whole noun group in the sentence. Write it on the line.

It was an old farmhouse with a beautiful garden.

_____

4. Add some words to make an interesting noun group.

(a) kitchen _____

(b) shed _____

5. Choose one or two interesting adjectives to describe each noun.

(a) smells   _____

(b) stories   _____

6. Add adjectives to make the sentences more descriptive.

(a) Grandad's _____ teacup was full of _____ tea.

(b) Nan gave us some _____ food to take home.

TEACHING WRITING STRATEGIES (Book 3)
www.prim-ed.com
978-1-912760-36-7

PRONOUNS, USING PRONOUNS, WHICH PRONOUN?

Name: _____ Date: _____

1. Circle the correct pronoun in the sentences.

(a) My skateboard isn't new but I think it is great.

(b) The boys went to the shops before they went home.

(c) My sister didn't want to go because she had too much homework.

2. Circle the correct pronoun in the sentences.

(a) When it is raining *we/I/they* get our feet wet jumping in puddles.

(b) My favourite day is Saturday because *us/I/they* play with my friends.

(c) Ben didn't wipe his feet before *we/he/they* came inside.

3. Choose a pronoun to write in each space.

> *mine*   *theirs*   *yours*

(a) I have my raincoat; if you're coming with me you will need _____.

(b) The other girls will need to bring _____ too.

(c) I lost my shoes and I think the ones you found could be _____.

4. Add 'who' or 'that'.

(a) The shoes _____ I found are very small.

(b) The girl _____ found them gave them to the teacher.

5. Change all the highlighted nouns to pronouns. Write the new text.

*The first time I rode a horse was on a farm. **The horse** was only small and **the horse** behaved. The teacher led me around. **The teacher** told me I was holding the reins too tightly and I had to let go of **the reins** a bit.*

_____

_____

_____

_____

Name: _____ Date _____

1. Choose the best verb to complete each sentence.

hammer   *tumbled*   *sparkling*

(a) The surfer came off his board and was _____ around by the wave.

(b) Why did the police _____ on the surfer's door?

(c) We love seeing the sun _____ on the ocean.

2. Write each sentence using more descriptive verbs.

(a) We <u>went</u> down the river in our canoe.

_____

(b) The fishermen <u>got</u> some fish early yesterday morning.

_____

(c) When it's raining, I like <u>to go</u> in puddles.

_____

(d) The roaring water <u>went</u> over the waterfall.

_____

3. Add an adverbial to tell *how*.

(a) The waves crashed _____.

(b) Did you see the boys swimming _____?

4. Add an adverbial to tell *when*.

(a) Our family enjoyed their picnic _____.

(b) We drove home _____.

5. Add an adverbial to tell *where*.

(a) The frightened child sat _____.

(b) The slippery rocks were _____.

Name: _____ Date _____

1. Underline the verbs. Write 'past', 'present' or 'future' after each sentence.

(a) I will visit the Cocos Islands one day soon. _____

(b) The Clunies Ross family sold the islands to Australia.
_____

(c) There is an airstrip on the Cocos Islands. _____

2. Correct the verb tense and write it on the line.

(a) There will be a cable station in 1901. _____

(b) In the past, convicts are sent to work on Cocos. _____

(c) Tourists come to dive there last year. _____

3. Write the past tense of each verb on the line.

(a) I enjoy snorkelling. _____

(b) The cyclone season will come in January. _____

(c) I swim in the ocean every day. _____

4. Write each verb with a helper verb.

(a) seen _____ (b) done _____ (c) been _____

5. Circle the verb, then draw a line under *who* or *what* is doing the action.

(a) The visitors landed at midday.

(b) Every morning, the teachers go to Home Island on the ferry.

(c) Huge crabs could be seen all over the road.

6. Put a tick or cross after each sentence to show if the verb group is correct.

(a) Yesterday, the trip across to Home Island is taking 30 minutes. ☐

(b) We have seen lots of fish in the water. ☐

(c) The yachts was anchored near the island. ☐

(d) The men all had to work very hard. ☐

(e) Regular flights is coming to the islands. ☐

UNIT 5   SENTENCES, WORD ORDER, QUESTIONS

Focus

Sentence structure — sentences, word order, questions

Progression

Recognise
Pupils will recognise a sentence from modelled examples.

Choose
Pupils will choose a variety of sentences from given examples, with teacher support.

Use
Pupils will use sentences in self-written sentences and paragraphs.

Definition of Terms

A **sentence** is a set of words that makes sense by itself. It may be a statement, a question, an exclamation or a command.

Introduction

Good writers improve their writing by planning sentences and paragraphs.

Introduction

- Discuss the text title with the class.
- What do they think the text is about?
- Discuss different types of boats and what they are used for.
- Discuss the different types of imaginative text and the features of recounts.
- Read the text with or to the class.

Sentences – Page 33

- Read and discuss the definition at the top of the page.
- Explain that sentences can be either long or short and that the number of words in a set of words is unrelated to whether or not it qualifies as a sentence.
- Discuss different types of sentences—statements, questions, commands and exclamations—and how each is punctuated.
- Explain that a small change in a sentence can make a big difference to its meaning or give the opposite meaning; for example, adding prefixes to make antonyms or the word 'not' to change from a positive to a negative.
- Discuss words with opposite meanings (antonyms) and ask for examples.
- Work through the activities with the class as a whole, ensuring they understand what is required of them.
- Work with those requiring additional assistance while the remainder of the class work independently on the activities.

Word Order – Page 34

- Explain that word order can make a difference.
- Ask for examples of the order in which pairs of words are usually said; for example, pepper and salt vs salt and pepper, and for why this happens (the more important comes first, sounds better, traditional, easier to say etc.).
- Ask pupils to explain why some of the words in the jumbled sentences have capital letters and ask what they need to add after the last word.
- Work through the activities with the class as a whole, ensuring they understand what is required of them.
- Work with those requiring additional assistance while the remainder of the class work independently on the activities.

Questions – Page 35

- Discuss with pupils the definition at the top of the page.
- Work with the class as a whole, demonstrating methods of changing statements to questions. Ensure pupils are comfortable with this concept.
- Work with those requiring additional assistance while the remainder of the class work independently on the activities.

TEACHING WRITING STRATEGIES (Book 3)
www.prim-ed.com
978-1-912760-36-7

UNIT 5   SENTENCES, WORD ORDER, QUESTIONS

ANSWERS

Sentences – Page 33

1. (a) and (c) require full stops.

2. (a) I really do not like the idea of going fast in a boat.
   (b) Most boats will not cost a lot of money to buy.

3. (a) unloved
   (b) impossible
   (c) unwelcome
   (d) uncomfortable

4. Teacher check

5. Possible answers may include:
   (a) forget
   (b) answer/statement
   (c) after
   (d) sell

6. Teacher check

Word Order – Page 34

1. Suggested answers
   (a) ✓   (b) ✗   (c) ✗

2. (a) ✓   (b) ✗   (c) ✗

3. (a) The children want a fast boat.
   (b) Mum wants her friends on the boat.
   (c) Dad just wants to go fishing.

4. (a) When the weather is good, Dad likes to go fishing.
   (b) If Dad buys a fast boat, the children will have fun.
   (c) Whenever the the weather is good, their boat will be used.

Questions – Page 35

1. (a) full stop
   (b) full stop
   (c) question mark
   (d) question mark

2. Teacher check

3. (a) She wanted to use the boat for tubing and waterskiing.
   (b) The narrator wanted to use the boat for racing along the waves, waterskiing and wanted to drive it.

4. Teacher check

ASSESSMENT ANSWERS

Assessment Activity – Page 54

1. (a) ✓   (b) ✓   (c) ✗   (d) ✗

2. (a) I do not think it would be great to try waterskiing.
   (b) I do not like being out on the water.

3. (a) ✗,✓   (b) ✗,✓

4. (a) Slow down when the waves are big.
   (b) Hold on when the sea is rough.

5. (a) question mark
   (b) full stop
   (c) question mark
   (d) full stop

6. (a) How fast is it?/Is it fast enough to for a skier?
   (b) Is it a good fishing boat?/What kind of fishing boat is it?
   (c) What colour is it?

Class Record Sheet – Page vii

ASSESSMENT WRITING

- **Paragraph Topic** – *The Boat I'd Like to Have*
- **Focus: Sentence Structure** – *sentences, word order, questions*

Self-evaluation – Page xiii

WHAT KIND OF BOAT?

1. When Dad came home and told us that he had just decided to buy a boat, we were all very excited.

2. 'How wonderful!' said Mum. 'I'd love to be able to take some friends out and just float around and relax out on the water. We'll have to make sure we have some great music to listen to on the boat. And, of course, we'll need a fridge for our food and drinks and some comfortable chairs or sun lounges. A good canopy to shade us from the sun is important, too.' She smiled and I could see that she was happily imagining herself relaxing on our boat with her friends.

3. Dad didn't say anything. He just sat there scratching his head and looking thoughtful.

4. 'That's great, Dad', said my sister, before I had a chance to open my mouth. 'I've always wanted to have a go on one of those big tubes they tow behind a boat. It looks such a fun thing to do. Perhaps I could learn to waterski. That's even more awesome. Perhaps I could get some skis for Christmas.'

5. Dad just continued sitting there staring at us with a strange look on his face.

6. Then at last I had a chance to ask Dad a question. 'What size motor will you get, Dad? We'll need something pretty big if we want to get any speed out of it.' I could just see us racing along, jumping across the waves and landing with a thump. It would be really exciting. 'I'd love to waterski, too.' I was built for speed and I was imagining myself zooming along behind the boat, doing tight turns on a ski or standing up on my surfboard.

7. 'How old do I have to be before I'm allowed to get a licence to drive a boat?' I asked, hoping it wouldn't be too long. 'It would be very useful to have a second driver you know.'

8. Dad just looked from one of us to the others and back again. Finally, he gave a big sigh and said quietly, 'Well, I was thinking of a little dinghy I could put on top of my car to go fishing in'.

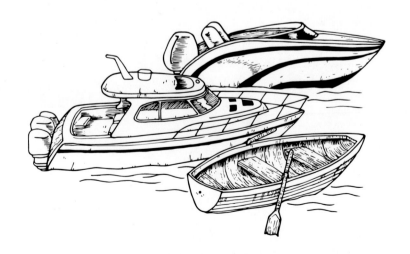

TEACHING WRITING STRATEGIES (Book 3)
www.prim-ed.com

978-1-912760-36-7

SENTENCES

A **sentence** is a set of words that makes sense by itself.

1. Put a full stop in the boxes after a sentence and nothing in the other boxes.

    (a) Water skiing is fun ☐   (b) At first it's quite hard to ☐

    (c) Hold on tight ☐   (d) You will need to go fast if you want ☐

2. Change the meaning of the sentence by adding the word 'not' or 'do not'.

    (a) I really like the idea of going very fast in a boat.

    _____

    _____

    (b) Most boats will cost a lot of money to buy.

    _____

    _____

3. Change the meaning by adding 'un' or 'im' in front of of the words.

    (a) loved _____   (b) possible _____

    (c) welcome _____   (d) comfortable _____

4. Write an interesting sentence using one of the words you wrote in Question 3.

    _____

    _____

    _____

5. Change the meaning by writing a word with the opposite meaning.

    (a) learn _____   (b) question _____

    (c) before _____   (d) buy _____

6. Write an interesting sentence using one of the words you wrote in Question 5.

    _____

    _____

    _____

WORD ORDER

If we change the order, some pairs of words sound odd to us.

1. Put a tick or a cross to show which pairs sound correct.

    (a) big and little ☐   (b) chips and fish ☐   (c) white and black ☐

2. Word order makes a difference. Do the following sentences make sense? Add a tick or a cross.

    (a) Boats come in all different shapes and sizes. ☐

    (b) you want a fast boat If you need a bigger motor. ☐

    (c) It's not a good idea a boat to take out in stormy weather. ☐

3. Change the order of the words so the sentence makes sense.

    (a) The fast children a want boat.

    _____

    (b) Mum friends wants her on the boat.

    _____

    (c) Dad go just wants fishing. to

    _____

4. Change the order of the words so the sentence has a different beginning.

    (a) Dad likes to go fishing when the weather is good.

    _____

    _____

    (b) The children will have fun if Dad buys a fast boat.

    _____

    _____

    (c) Their boat will be used whenever the weather is good.

    _____

    _____

QUESTIONS

> A **question** needs an answer. It is always written with a question mark.

1. Add question marks at the end of questions and full stops after any sentences.

    (a) I don't know when Dad will buy a boat ☐

    (b) When it's not windy, we will try waterskiing ☐

    (c) When is the best time to ski ☐

    (d) When would you like me to come and help you ☐

2. (a) Change a sentence from Question 1 and write it as a question.

    _____

    _____

    (b) Write any new words you added to the question.

    _____

    _____

Answer the questions from the text.

3. (a) What did the boy's sister want to use the boat for?

    _____

    _____

    (b) What would the narrator like to use the boat for?

    _____

    _____

4. (a) Write a question about waterskiing.

    _____

    _____

    (b) Write a question about a boat.

    _____

    _____

UNIT 6   SENTENCE BEGINNINGS

Focus

Sentence structure – sentence beginnings

Progression

Recognise
Pupils will recognise a variety of interesting sentence beginnings from modelled examples.

Choose
Pupils will choose a variety of sentences from given examples, with teacher support.

Use
Pupils will use interesting sentence beginnings in self-written sentences.

Definition of Terms

Verbs or 'doing' words show actions or states of being or having.

A **Verb group** is a verb combined with other, auxiliary, verbs.

Adverbials are words or groups of words that add information, usually to a verb or verb group. They can tell how (manner), when (time) or where (place) something happens. Adverbs can modify (add information to) any words that are not nouns or pronouns. (These are modified by adjectives.)

Introduction

Good writers improve their writing by using a variety of different, interesting sentence beginnings.

Introduction

- Discuss the text title with the class.
- What do pupils think the text could be about?
- Identify the number of paragraphs and discuss the use of subheadings.
- Explain that organising information into paragraphs helps a reader to understand.
- Identify the text type and discuss the features of informative text.

Sentences Beginnings – When and Where? – Page 39

- Discuss as a class, possible reasons why a writer tries to begin sentences in an interesting way.
- Discuss starting sentences by telling when and where. Give some examples.
- Work through the activities with the class as a whole, ensuring they understand what is required of them. Work with those requiring additional assistance while the remainder of the class work independently on the activities.

Sentence Beginnings – How? – Page 40

- Discuss with pupils the way a sentence can start by telling **how** something is happening. Work through an example on the board; for example, *Hurriedly …*
- Ask, 'Who is likely to do something *hurriedly?*' Discuss selected possible answers with pupils.
- Select one appropriate response – say, 'Pupils'. Discuss what pupils might be doing *hurriedly.*
- Revise the concept of verb groups as a combination that gives greater meaning.
- Work with those requiring additional assistance while the remainder of the class work independently on the activities.

Sentence Beginnings – Choosing the Best, and Then … – Page 41

- Pupils could discuss the sentence beginnings with a partner to choose the one they consider to be the best.
- Discuss with pupils the undesirable results of repeated use of a conjunction ('and then') – repetitive, overlong sentences; uninteresting writing.
- Ask how pupils could overcome this problem. Discuss answers.
- Elicit the solution of starting a new sentence, changing the word order and using a variety of conjunctions.
- Work with those requiring additional assistance while the remainder of the class work independently on the activities.

ANSWERS

Sentence Beginnings – When and Where? – Page 39

   1.–3. Teacher check

Sentence Beginnings – How? – Page 40

   1.–2. Teacher check

Sentence Beginnings – Choosing the Best, And Then ... Page 41

   1.–3. Teacher check

ASSESSMENT ANSWERS

Assessment Activity – Page 55

   1.–6. Teacher check

Class Record Sheet – Page vii

ASSESSMENT WRITING

- **Paragraph Topic** – *An Amazing Sight*
- **Focus: Sentence Structure** – *sentence beginnings*

Self-evaluation – Page xiii

RIVERS OF ICE

What are glaciers?

1. Glaciers are rivers of ice moving downhill to the sea. Most glaciers move very slowly, but some do speed up. One glacier in Pakistan moved 12 kilometres in three months! However, that is unusually fast.

How are glaciers made?

2. When snow is falling on a mountain faster than it melts, it is squeezed down until it becomes very hard ice. This can take thousands and thousands of years. The hard ice then starts to move downhill.

What happens to the land?

3. As glaciers travel they grind away the land around them. This makes deep u-shaped valleys. When it becomes warmer and the ice melts, these valleys remain. Then they usually fill up with water. The famous fiords of Norway were once filled by glaciers. Now they are so deep that huge cruise ships take tourists sailing through them.

What is in a glacier?

4. The ice in a glacier is made of fresh water. It is mostly very pure, but ash from ancient volcanoes may have left dark streaks in the ice. There can also be dirt that has been scraped up from the earth. Rocks and boulders can also be picked up and carried along on its journey. These can be seen along the sides of the glacier.

What happens when a glacier reaches the sea?

5. When a glacier finally reaches water, huge chunks of ice break off and fall into the water. This is called 'calving'. The giant splash and 'b-o-o-m' is a very spectacular thing to see and hear. When ice crashes down and floats away, it becomes an iceberg.

Where are glaciers found?

6. There are glaciers on every continent on Earth, except one – Australia. Scientists say that glaciers cover about 10% of Earth's surface and hold about 75% of Earth's fresh water. If all that ice melted, Earth's surface would be covered by water about 5 metres deep!

TEACHING WRITING STRATEGIES (Book 3)
www.prim-ed.com
978-1-912760-36-7

SENTENCES BEGINNINGS – WHEN AND WHERE?

Sentence beginnings are important. Sentences should start in different, interesting ways.

1. Complete the sentences. They all start by telling *when* something happened.

(a) When a glacier reaches water, _____

_____

(b) While I was watching, _____

_____

(c) After the ice breaks off, _____

_____

2. Add an interesting sentence beginning telling *when* each thing happened.

(a) _____ we went whale watching.

(b) _____ the girl went to the beach.

(c) _____ they spotted a whale.

3. Write interesting sentences starting with *where* something happened.

(a) Far out to sea, _____

_____

(b) Close to the ship, _____

_____

(c) At the sides of the glacier, _____

_____

SENTENCE BEGINNINGS – HOW?

1. Complete the sentences which start with *how* something is happening. Use descriptive verbs to make them interesting.

(a) With a huge splash, _____

_____

(b) Slowly, _____

_____

(c) Amazingly, _____

_____

(d) Unexpectedly, _____

_____

(e) With a gasp of surprise, _____

_____

2. A verb can also be a good sentence beginning. Complete the sentences.

(a) Waking up early, I _____

_____

(b) Floating in the water was _____

_____

(c) Waiting patiently, we stood _____

_____

(d) Moving ever so slowly, _____

_____

(e) Expecting to be amazed, we _____

_____

SENTENCES BEGINNINGS – CHOOSING THE BEST

1. Read each paragraph of the text. Underline the sentence beginning you think is the best one in each paragraph. Write the beginnings you chose from each paragraph.

(a) Paragraph 1

_____

(b) Paragraph 2

_____

(c) Paragraph 3

_____

(d) Paragraph 4

_____

(e) Paragraph 5

_____

(f) Paragraph 6

_____

2. Choose one of the sentence beginnings from Question 1 and use it to start a sentence of your own. Make it interesting.

_____

_____

AND THEN ...

Instead of putting a full stop and starting a new sentence, many writers add 'and then' and just keep on writing. This is a boring way to write.

3. Rewrite the text. You could start a new sentence instead of writing 'and then', or you could join two sentences with a better conjunction; for example, 'as', 'while', 'before' or 'after'.

The ship sailed silently towards the glacier and then we could see tiny icebergs in the water and then the water became slushy and then we stopped near the glacier and then we all waited to see some ice calving.

_____

_____

_____

_____

UNIT 7 CONJUNCTIONS

Focus

Sentence structure – conjunctions

Progression

Recognise
Pupils will recognise a conjunction from modelled examples.

Choose
Pupils will choose conjunctions from given examples, with teacher support.

Use
Pupils will use appropriate conjunctions in supplied and self-written sentences.

Definition of Terms

Verbs or 'doing' words show actions or states of being or having. A **verb group** is a verb combined with other, auxiliary, verbs. **Adverbials** are words or groups of words that add information, usually to a verb or verb group. They can tell how (manner), when (time) or where (place) something happens. Adverbs can modify (add information to) any words that are not nouns or pronouns. (These are modified by adjectives.)

Introduction

Good writers improve their writing by improving sentence structure using appropriate conjunctions.

Teacher Information

Conjunctions:
• enable a writer to build and combine ideas and to avoid repetition; and
• can be placed between two clauses or at the beginning of a longer sentence.

The position of the conjunction can help readers to know which part of the sentence is the focus.

LESSON NOTES AND PLANS

Introduction

• Discuss the text title.
• What do pupils think the text is about.
• Introduce the term 'conjunctions' and explain that they enable a writer to combine ideas and to avoid repetition; for example, *They ate fish. They ate chips. = They ate fish and chips.*
• Read the text with or to the class.
• Ask pupils to identify the text type and discuss the purpose.
• Identify some of the conjunctions used in the text.

Joining Sentences – Conjunctions – Page 45

• Read and discuss the definition at the top of the page.
• Discuss how sentences can be joined by using conjunctions.
• Work with those requiring additional assistance while the remainder of the class work independently on the activities.

Using Conjunctions – Page 46

• Review pupils' understanding of the term 'conjunction' and ask them to provide examples.
• List words or phrases that can be used as conjunctions.
• Discuss how conjunctions can be used to begin a sentence or to join two smaller ones.
• Work through the activities with the class as a whole, ensuring they understand what is required of them.
• Work with those requiring additional assistance while the remainder of the class work independently on the activities.
• In pairs, pupils can share the sentences they wrote in Question 4.

Which Conjunctions? – Page 47

• Discuss and list conjunctions of time with the class and explain why it is important to use the correct one.
• Explain that conjunctions can be used to tell that one event caused the other. Conjunctions showing cause will be used in Question 2.
• In Question 3, conjunctions are used to compare and contrast.
• Work through the activities with the class as a whole, ensuring they understand what is required of them.
• Work with those requiring additional assistance while the remainder of the class work independently on the activities.
• In pairs, pupils can share the sentences they wrote in Question 3.

UNIT 7   CONJUNCTIONS

ANSWERS

Joining Sentences – Conjunctions – Page 45

1. (a) and, as
   (b) Teacher check

2. (a) When
   (b) If
   (c) Before
   (d) At the beginning of the sentences.

3. Answers will vary. Possible answer: Gemma was upset because she had been having an argument.

4. (a) Gemma asked her mum if she could have her ears pierced.
   (b) Gemma thought she was old enough because she was ten.
   (c) Mum kept saying no, but Gemma kept asking her.
   (d) full stops, capital letters

Using Conjunctions – Page 46

1. (a) 2
   (b) Teacher check
   (c) running into her room
   (d) Mum and Dad
   (e) instead of

2. (a) that
   (b) when
   (c) when

3.–4. Teacher check

Which Conjunctions? – Page 47

1. Possible answers
   (a) After she spoke to her mother, she was upset.
   (b) After her mother said no, she wrote a letter.
   (c) She gave her parents the letter after she wrote it.

2.–3. Teacher check

Assessment Activity – Page 56

1. (a) because
   (b) after
   (c) if

2. Gemma thought she was responsible because she looked after her pets.

3. Answers may include:
   (a) Gemma hoped to go shopping with Nanna after she had her ears pierced.
   (b) Gemma waited while her parents read her letter.
   (c) She wanted earrings with green stones.

4. (a) after
   (b) before

5. Teacher check

Class Record Sheet – Page vii

ASSESSMENT WRITING

- **Paragraph Topic** – *Please, Mum*
- **Focus: Sentence Structure** – conjunctions

Self-evaluation – Page xiii

PLEASE MUM!

1. 'But Mum!' wailed Gemma. 'It's not fair, why can't I have my ears pierced?' Gemma's mum just shook her head and walked away.

2. Gemma was upset. She and her mum had been having this same argument since she was six. But it was her tenth birthday on Saturday and she really thought it was about time she won the argument.

3. This time, instead of bursting into tears and running into her room, Gemma decided to try something different. She decided to write Mum and Dad a letter.

---

4. Dear Mum and Dad

5. I'll be ten on Friday. I think you should let me have my ears pierced as a birthday present.

6. I am a very responsible girl who looks after three pets and never forgets to feed them. I will be able to look after my ears well myself. I won't forget. They won't become infected like my friend Kate's did.

7. It's school holidays, which is a good time to have them done. I'll have plenty of time to look after them. I'll put antiseptic on them three times every day. By the time we go back to school, they'll be fine.

8. Nanna is always worried about what presents to buy me. It will be easy for her to find new earrings for me every year. The shops have thousands of different ones.

9. I really am growing up. I know I have been rude to you about this in the past. I'm sorry that I behaved like a silly, little girl. I promise when I'm ten, things will change. I will feel much more grown-up when I have pierced ears.

10. So, please let me have my ears pierced. I'm old enough and responsible enough already. There is no need to leave it for another year ... and think how many arguments you'll be saving yourselves and how happy I'll be!

Your loving daughter
Gemma

 TEACHING WRITING STRATEGIES (Book 3)
www.prim-ed.com 978-1-912760-36-7

JOINING SENTENCES – CONJUNCTIONS

> **A conjunction joins two ideas.** For example:
> I had my ears pierced for my birthday. I was given earrings.
>
> I had my ears pierced for my birthday and was given earrings.
> As I had my ears pierced for my birthday, I was given earrings.

1. (a) List all the conjunctions used in the examples. _____

    (b) Write the sentence you think sounds the best. _____

_____

2. Circle the conjunctions in the sentences.

    (a) When you are twelve, you can have your ears pierced.

    (b) If I write you a letter, you might change your mind.

    (c) Before you make a decision, please read my letter.

    (d) Where in the sentences were the three conjunctions you circled?

_____

3. Join the two sentences using a conjunction.

Gemma was upset. She had been having an argument.

_____

4. Join the two sentences using a conjunction from the three words below.

          because   *if*   *but*

    (a) Gemma asked her mum. She could have her ears pierced.

_____

    (b) Gemma thought she was old enough. She was ten.

_____

    (c) Mum kept saying no. Gemma kept asking her.

_____

    (d) What punctuation was no longer needed when you joined the sentences?

_____

USING CONJUNCTIONS

1. Read Paragraph 3.

(a) How many sentences does it contain?_____

(b) Circle the two 'and' conjunctions in the paragraph.

(c) The first 'and' joins bursting into tears and _____.

(d) The second 'and' joins _____ and _____.

(e) The conjunction joining two ideas below is _____.

- bursting into tears and running into her room

- trying something different?

2. Which conjunction in Paragraph 9 joins:

(a) being sorry / behaving like a silly, little girl? _____

(b) being ten / things changing? _____

(c) feeling more grown-up / having pierced ears _____

3. Write an interesting sentence with two ideas using these words as conjunctions.

(a) unless _____

_____

(b) until _____

_____

(c) while _____

_____

4. Use these conjunctions to start a sentence joining two ideas.

(a) As soon as _____

_____

(b) Slowly, _____

_____

(c) Although _____

_____

978-1-912760-36-7

WHICH CONJUNCTIONS?

1. Some writers use incorrect conjunctions of time.
Circle the conjunction then write the sentence correctly.

   (a) She was upset before she spoke to her mother.

   _____

   _____

   (b) Before her mother said no, she wrote a letter.

   _____

   _____

   (c) She gave her parents the letter before she wrote it.

   _____

   _____

2. Explain how one event is caused by another by using the conjunction in the middle of a sentence joining two ideas. For example: I smile and laugh **when** I am happy.

   (a) when _____

   _____

   (b) I left my reading book at home because _____

   _____

   (c) because _____

   _____

3. Write sentences using the conjunction to compare two different things.

   (a) Although he is lazy, he _____

   _____

   _____

   (b) Although _____

   _____

UNIT 8   PARAGRAPHS

Focus

Sentence structure – paragraphs

Progression

Recognise

Pupils will recognise a paragraph from modelled examples.

Choose

Pupils will choose ideas and sentences for paragraphs with teacher support.

Use

Pupils will choose information for paragraphs in supplied and self-written paragraphs.

Definition of Terms

Paragraphs are sections of writing dealing with a particular subject or point, beginning on a new line.

A **topic sentence** is a sentence in a paragraph that introduces the main idea of that paragraph. It is often, but not always, the first sentence in the paragraph.

Introduction

Good writers improve their writing by improving sentence structure in paragraphs.

Teacher Information

Paragraphs enable a writer to organise and combine ideas to aid comprehension.

A **topic sentence** connects ideas within a paragraph.

Introduction

- Discuss the text title and what it might be about.
- What genre do they think it is?
- What are some of the features of fairy tales? Which fairy tale is it most likely to be?
- Read the text with or to the class.
- Discuss the confusion between *Little Red Riding Hood* and *Goldilocks*.

Paragraphs – Page 51

- Read and discuss the definition at the top of the page.
- Read Paragraph 1. What does the introduction tell the reader?
- Work through the activities with the class as a whole, ensuring they understand what is required of them.
- Work with those requiring additional assistance while the remainder of the class work independently on the activities.

Planning Paragraphs – Page 52

- Read and discuss the information at the top of the page.
- Discuss different types of bears, real and imaginary, and what they know about them (using the questions from Question 2 as a guide).
- Explain that on this page pupils will be planning a paragraph about bears.
- Discuss their choice of bears and reasons for choosing, explaining that it would be advisable to choose a bear they have some knowledge of.
- Read the questions in Question 2 with the class and explain that the answer to one of these questions should be the topic for their paragraph about the bear they selected.
- Provide opportunities for pupils to share and discuss their opening sentences from Question 4(b).

Writing a Paragraph – Page 53

- Discuss the differences between life in the city and life in the country.
- Remind pupils that the sentences in a paragraph all should be about the same thing and they need to be in some order.
- Provide opportunities for pupils to read and discuss their paragraphs in small groups. They should decide how appropriate the information is to that particular paragraph.

UNIT 8

PARAGRAPHS

ANSWERS

Paragraphs – Page 51

1. (a) 4
   (b) Father Bear was away.

2. (a) Paragraph 11
   (b) 4
   (c) No

3. (a) Paragraph 7
   (b) Paragraph 15
   (c) Paragraph 17
   (d) Paragraph 11
   (e) Paragraph 6

4. Teacher check

5. (a) True
   (b) False
   (c) True
   (d) True

Planning Paragraphs — Page 52

1. Teacher check

2. No answer required.

3.–4. Teacher check

Writing a Paragraph — Page 53

1. (a) Teacher check. Possible answer: Moving from the country to the city.
   (b) Teacher check. Suggested order: 2, 1 3
   (c) Teacher check

2. Teacher check

ASSESSMENT ANSWERS

Assessment Activity – Page 57

1. (a) Yes
   (b) Yes
   (c) Yes
   (d) Yes

2. Teacher check

Class Record Sheet – Page vii

ASSESSMENT WRITING

- **Paragraph Topic** – *A Mixed-up Fairy Tale*
- **Focus: Sentence Structure** – *paragraphs*

Self-evaluation – Page xiii

BIG, BLACK RIDING BOOTS

1. Once upon a time there were two bears.

2. No, there were three bears: Mama Bear, Father Bear and Baby Bear.

3. No, there were two bears. Father Bear was away. He had a job as a fly-in, fly-out worker. He only came home for one week every month.

4. They lived in an apartment close to the centre of the city.

5. No, they lived in a cottage in the woods.

6. No, it was too scary living in the woods by themselves, so Mama Bear and Baby Bear moved to the city.

7. Then one day, a hungry, little boy broke into their apartment.

8. No, it was a little girl and she just walked in because the door was open.

9. No, nobody would ever leave their doors open in the city. He was hungry, so he opened the freezer.

10. No, she tried all the bears' porridge before she ate up all of Baby Bear's.

11. No, there wasn't any porridge. He found a frozen pizza, cooked it in the microwave and ate it. Then he tried two chairs. Baby Bear's chair was just the right size, but it fell over and broke when he dragged it over to the cupboard and stood on it.

12. No, she sat on it and it broke.

13. No, he was trying to get some more food out of the cupboard and it fell over and broke. After he'd eaten more food, he went to have a rest on the settee and watch television.

14. No, she went upstairs and tried the beds. She fell asleep in Baby Bear's bed.

15. No, he couldn't be bothered walking upstairs, so he just flopped on the settee. Then the smoke alarm went off. It was so loud it woke him up.

16. No, the bears came home and she woke up. She raced outside and ran home.

17. No, he fled the scene before anyone came in to check on the fire alarm. You know, you're very mixed up! You must be thinking about *Little Red Riding Hood*! Don't you know anything about fairy tales?

18. Well … I thought I did!

PARAGRAPHS

> A **paragraph** is one or more sentences about the same thing. The first sentence of a paragraph often tells what the paragraph is about.

1. (a) How many sentences are there in Paragraph 3? _____

   (b) Tick the sentence that tells what the paragraph is mainly about.

   • No, there were two bears. ☐   • Father Bear was away. ☐

2. (a) Which paragraph is about Big, Black Riding Boots' eating pizza? _____

   (b) How many sentences are in this paragraph? _____

   (c) Does this paragraph explain why he stood on the chair? _____

3. Read the sentences. Which paragraphs would you put them in?

   (a) The little boy's name was Big, Black Riding Boots and he was bad. _____

   (b) The settee was very comfortable and before long he fell asleep. _____

   (c) There wasn't a fire, so it must have just been a false alarm. _____

   (d) The cupboard was quite high and he couldn't reach it. _____

   (e) It was frightening in the woods. _____

4. (a) Write one of the paragraphs with only one sentence.

   _____

   (b) Write another sentence for this paragraph.

   _____

5. What do you know about paragraphs? Write 'true' or 'false'.

   (a) The first sentence must start on a new line with a capital letter. _____

   (b) A paragraph must have two sentences. _____

   (c) The sentences in one paragraph should all be about the same topic. _____

   (d) The first sentence must always tell what the paragraph is about. _____

PLANNING PARAGRAPHS

> A writer needs to plan *what* will be in each paragraph. The words *where, when, what, why* and *how* help a writer to make a good plan.

1. In this lesson you will be planning a paragraph in a text about a bear.

   (a) The bear I choose to write about is _____

   _____

   (b) I chose this bear because _____

   _____

2. Think about the bear you chose and how much you know about it.
Think how you would answer the questions:

   • What does it looks like?   • What does it do?

   • What does it eat?   • Where does it live?

   • How does it move?   • What would I like to know about it?

3. Write the first sentence of the introduction telling what the text is about and
why this bear is interesting.

Introduction:

_____

_____

_____

4. (a) Think about what you want the next paragraph to be about.

     The topic for the next paragraph is _____.

   (b) Write the first sentence for your paragraph.

    _____

    _____

   (c) Does this sentence tell what your paragraph is about? _____

   (d) What other information will you add to this paragraph?

    _____

    _____

TEACHING WRITING STRATEGIES (Book 3)
www.prim-ed.com

978-1-912760-36-7

WRITING A PARAGRAPH

1. The first paragraph in a story about moving from the country to live in the city starts with this sentence.

> It took us all day to drive to the city and the traffic was terrible.

(a) What do you think this paragraph will be about?

_____

(b) Write 1, 2 and 3 in the boxes to show the best order for the sentences.

• There were cars everywhere and Mum couldn't find anywhere to park. ☐

• Finally, we were outside our apartment block in High Street. ☐

• I could see she was tired and this was making her grumpy. ☐

(c) Complete the next sentence for this paragraph.

We all sighed with relief. There was a small sign on the side of the

building that said RESIDENTS' CAR PARK, so Mum _____

_____

_____

2. This story now needs the next paragraph.

(a) What do you think it should be about?

_____

_____

(b) Write this paragraph. Make sure the sentences are all about the same thing.

_____

_____

_____

_____

_____

_____

_____

Name: _____ Date: _____

1. Is it a sentence? Put a tick or a cross in the box.

  (a) Look at that boat ☐   (b) It is going very fast ☐

  (c) If it slows down ☐   (d) I don't think it is fast enough for ☐

2. Change the meaning by adding 'not' or 'do not'.

  (a) I think it would be great to try waterskiing.

  _____

  (b) I like being out on the water.

  _____

3. Which one sounds better? Put a tick or a cross in the box.

  (a) chips and fish ☐   fish and chips ☐

  (b) white and black ☐   black and white ☐

4. Change the order of the words so the sentence makes sense.

  (a) Slow big. down the when waves are

  _____

  (b) Hold the sea is rough. when on

  _____

5. Add question marks at the end of questions and full stops after any sentences.

  (a) Which boat shall I buy ☐   (b) I think they are all too small ☐

  (c) How fast does that one go ☐   (d) I don't know why you like that one ☐

6. Write the sentence as a question.

  (a) It is fast enough for a skier. _____

  (b) It is a good fishing boat. _____

  (c) It is blue and white. _____

Name: _____ Date: _____

1. Complete the sentence. It starts by telling *when* something happened.

Early that morning, we _____

2. Add an interesting sentence beginning by telling *when* this happened.

_____ *, the ship approached the glacier.*

3. Complete the sentence which starts by telling *where* something happened.

On the horizon, _____

4. Complete the sentence which starts by telling *how* something is happening.

With a huge b-o-o-m, the _____

_____

5. Complete the sentence beginning with a verb.

(a) *Gazing at the glacier, we* _____

_____

(b) *Dropping into the water with* _____

_____

(c) *Gasping with amazement, the passengers* _____

_____

6. Write the sentence without using 'and then'. You can change the word order.

We spent a whole day watching the glacier and then we sailed out
of the bay.

_____

_____

CONJUNCTIONS

Name: _____ Date: _____

1. Circle the conjunctions in the sentences.

   (a) Mum wouldn't let her have her ears pierced because she was too young.

   (b) She hoped Mum would change her mind after she read the letter.

   (c) Nanna would be happy if she knew what to buy Gemma.

2. Use a conjunction to connect these two ideas.

   Gemma thought she was responsible.   *She looked after her pets.*

   _____

3. Join two sentences using a conjunction below.
   You will need to cross out some words and change the punctuation.

   after   *with*   *while*

   (a) Gemma hoped to go shopping with Nanna.
        She had her ears pierced.

   (b) Gemma waited. Her parents read her letter.

   (c) She wanted earrings. She wanted green stones.

4. Use the correct conjunction of time.

   (a) Gemma gave the letter to Mum and Dad _____ she wrote it.

   (b) She wanted her ears pierced _____ she was twelve.

5. Use the conjunction to connect two interesting ideas in a sentence.

   (a) while _____

        _____

   (b) when _____

        _____

   (c) if _____

        _____

Name: _____ Date: _____

1. Read the paragraph.

Fairy Tales

No fairy tales are ever exactly the same. This is because they have been told and retold to children for hundreds of years. Some people change fairy tales because they want to, others forget the story and just make up bits for themselves.

(a) Does the first sentence tell what this paragraph is about? Yes ☐ No ☐

(b) Does the rest of the paragraph add further information? Yes ☐ No ☐

(c) Do you think the first sentence introduces the topic well? Yes ☐ No ☐

(d) Are all the sentences about the same thing? Yes ☐ No ☐

2. Think about the next paragraph. It is going to be about one fairy tale and some of the different ways it ends.

(a) Which is your fairy tale? _____

(b) Use the box to make notes about this fairy tale for your paragraph.
Think: Who is it about? What happened in the end? What is a different ending?

```



```

(c) Write the first sentence for your paragraph.

_____

_____

(d) Complete your paragraph. (Use the back of the page if you need more space.)

_____

_____

_____

UNIT 9   USING PUNCTUATION IN SENTENCES

Focus

Punctuation – using punctuation in sentences

Progression

Recognise
Pupils will recognise specified punctuation from modelled examples.

Choose
Pupils will choose appropriate punctuation for sentences, with teacher support.

Use
Pupils will correctly punctuate supplied and self-written sentences.

Definition of Terms

A **sentence** is a set of words that makes sense by itself. It may be a statement, a command, a question or an exclamation.

Capital letters are used at the beginning of a new sentence and for proper nouns.

A **full stop** is used at the end of a sentence.

A **question mark** is used at the end of a question.

An **exclamation mark** is used at the end of an exclamation.

Proper nouns are nouns used for naming a *particular* person, place or thing.

Introduction

Good writers improve their writing by using correct punctuation.

Teacher Information

Punctuation enables a writer to more fully and accurately communicate with the reader by making the writing more understandable.

LESSON NOTES AND PLANS

Introduction
- Discuss punctuation and its importance.
- List different types of punctuation, what each one looks like and when it is used.

Do We Need Punctuation? – Page 60
- Set pupils to work in pairs to complete Questions 1 to 5.
- In small groups, discuss their answers to Question 5. How similar were they? Why?

Capital Letters – Page 61
- Read the definitions and the text and discuss.
- Ask 'What is missing?' List answers.
- Question pupils to obtain a clear definition of what full stops and proper nouns are.
- Emphasise that a capital letter is needed for *proper nouns*; for example, South Wales, River Nile, Washington.
- Work with those requiring additional assistance while the remainder of the class work independently on the activities.
- Encourage pupils in small groups or as a class to discuss their responses to Questions 2 and 4.

Short Sentences – Page 62
- Read the text at the top of the page.
- Ensure pupils are familiar with the features of a *sentence*, a *command,* an *exclamation* and a *question*, including their specific punctuation.
- Brainstorm other examples with the class.
- Explain that some sentences can be very short and the number of words doesn't affect whether or not a group of words is a sentence.
- Provide opportunities for pupils to discuss in pairs their answers to Question 3.

Is it Correct? – Page 63
- Discuss the punctuation required for beginning and ending sentences, proper nouns, questions, exclamations and commands.
- Provide examples.
- Explain that mum and dad only need a capital letter when used instead of their names; for example, *My mum and dad love boating – I asked Dad if we could stay longer on the river.*
- Work with those requiring additional assistance while the remainder of the class work independently on the activities.
- Pupils will benefit from the opportunity to check a partner's punctuation in his or her answer to Question 2.

UNIT 9 USING PUNCTUATION IN SENTENCES

ANSWERS

Do We Need Punctuation? – Page 60

1. Teacher check

2. (a) 4
(b) 3
(c) 1

3. Canada, down, deafening, air

4.–5. Teacher check

Capital Letters – Page 61

1. (a) Teacher check
(b) 6
(c) 5
(d) Canada, Toronto, CN Tower, Niagara Falls

2.–4. Teacher check

Short Sentences – Page 62

1. (a) a capital letter
(b) No
(c) question mark, full stop, exclamation mark

2. (a) Put on your shoes.
(b)–(d) Teacher check

3. Teacher check

Is it Correct? – Page 63

1. (a) I want to go up the tower in Toronto.
(b) Then we'll have to go to Niagara again, too.
(c) Would you like to come to Canada with us?
(d) That would be awesome!

2. Teacher check. Do you know how tall the CN Tower is? Dad said it was about 550 metres, which is as tall as a 147-storey building. Wow, that's awesome!

3. (a) True
(b) False
(c) True

4. (a) ✗
(b) ✓

Assessment Activity – Page 82

1. (a) Teacher check
(b) 5
(c) 2
(d) 2

2.–3. Teacher check

4. (a) ✗
(b) ✓
(c) ✗
(d) ✗
(e) ✓
(f) ✓

5. (a) What did you see there?
(b) We were soaking wet.
(c) Hold on!
(d) Put on this coat.

6. (a) ✓
(b) ✗
(c) ✓
(d) ✗
(e) ✓
(f) ✗

Class Record Sheet – Page viii

ASSESSMENT WRITING

• **Paragraph Topic** – *The Best Waterfall*
• **Focus: Punctuation** – *using punctuation in sentences*

Self-evaluation – Page xiii

Niagara Falls

Niagara Falls are the three most amazing waterfalls we saw while we were in canada there is so much water pouring down the noise it makes is deafening I couldn't believe how much mist there was from all the spray in the air this made very beautiful rainbows over the falls.

1. Read Niagara Falls aloud to a partner.

    (a) Was it easy for you to read? _____

    (b) Do you think your partner understood it? _____

    (c) What was missing from the story?

_____

2. Use a red pencil or pen to change some letters to capital letters.

    (a) How many did you need to change? _____

    (b) How many were at the beginning of a sentence? _____

    (c) How many were names of people or places _____

3. Add full stops. Which words did you put a full stop after?

_____

4. Read 'Niagara Falls' to your partner again.

    (a) Was it easier to read this time? _____

    (b) Do you think your partner understood it better this time? _____

5. (a) Do you think adding punctuation is a good thing to do? _____

    (b) Why do you think this? _____

_____

    (c) Which punctuation do you think is the most important for a writer to use? Why?

_____

_____

60
      TEACHING WRITING STRATEGIES (Book 3)
      www.prim-ed.com
      978-1-912760-36-7

Capital letters are used at the beginning of a new sentence and for proper nouns. Proper nouns are nouns used for the name of a person, place or thing. For example: **C**allum, **A**merica, **N**iagara **F**alls, **T**oronto

Toronto

while we were in canada we stayed in the city of toronto, which is the closest major city to Niagara Falls. It is famous for its very tall CN Tower, but we didn't have time to go up to the top. we took a bus tour from there to the falls. the tour took all day and it was dark when we arrived back in the city. it was a great day.

1. (a) Use a red pencil or pen to put capital letters in the text.

(b) How many capital letters did you need to add? _____

(c) How many sentences are in the text? _____

(d) Write the proper nouns from the text.

_____

2. (a) Write two sentences about a place someone you know likes to visit. Use capital letters to name the place and the person who enjoys going there.

_____

_____

_____

(b) How many proper nouns did you use in your sentences? _____

3. Write a proper noun that tells you the name of:

(a) a town _____   (b) a country _____

(c) a continent _____   (d) a river _____

(e) a month _____   (f) a building _____

4. Write an interesting sentence using a proper noun from Question 3.

_____

_____

SHORT SENTENCES

- Who's that?
- How awesome!
- Come on!
- Put on your shoes.
- Stir well.
- Do not run.
- Hurry up!
- What happened?
- Look at me!
- Who's coming?
- Don't look!
- Take care!

1. Read the short sentences. They are all sentences because they make sense by themselves.

(a) What do they all start with? _____

(b) Do they all use the same punctuation mark at the end? _____

(c) What are the three punctuation marks used at the end of these sentences?

_____

2. (a) Write the longest sentence.

_____

(b) Write one of the exclamations.

_____

(c) Write one of the commands.

_____

(d) Write one of the questions.

_____

3. (a) Write a question with fewer than five words.

_____

(b) Write an exclamation with three words.

_____

(c) Write a command with four words.

_____

1. **Find the two punctuation errors in each sentence. Write the sentence correctly.**

   (a) I want to go up the tower in toronto?

   _____

   (b) Then we'll have to go to niagara again, too!

   _____

   (c) Would you like to come to canada with us.

   _____

   (d) that would be awesome.

   _____

2. **Find and circle the punctuation errors. Write the paragraph correctly.**

   do you know how tall the CN Tower is. Dad said it was about
   550 metres, which is as tall as a 147-storey building. wow, that's
   awesome!

   _____

   _____

   _____

3. **Write 'true' or 'false'.**

   (a) Capital letters are needed for the months of the year. _____

   (b) The words 'spring' and 'winter' need capital letters. _____

   (c) The name *mrs jones* needs two capital letters. _____

4. **Put a tick in the box if the punctuation is correct.**

   (a) You can see the falls from the american side too. ☐

   (b) A tour guide told us they are more spectacular from the Canadian side. ☐

UNIT 10 FULL STOPS, CAPITAL LETTERS, COMMAS, DIRECT SPEECH

Focus

Punctuation – full stops, capital letters, commas, direct speech

Progression

Recognise
Pupils will recognise specified punctuation from modelled examples.

Choose
Pupils will choose appropriate punctuation for sentences, with teacher support.

Use
Pupils will correctly punctuate supplied and self-written sentences.

Definition of Terms

A **sentence** is a set of words that makes sense by itself. It may be a statement, a command, a question or an exclamation.

A **full stop** is used to show the end of a sentence.

A **comma** is a punctuation mark used to show small breaks in a sentence.

Quotation marks are used to set off the actual words spoken or thought.

Introduction

Good writers improve their writing by using correct punctuation.

Teacher Information

Punctuation enables a writer to more fully and accurately communicate with the reader.

Note: There is more than one method of punctuating direct speech. (Two different methods are given in the Answers.) Whichever method is chosen, it must be consistently used.

A comma is used before the coordinating conjunction (the Oxford comma or serial comma) in some publications. It is not incorrect to use it this way, but it is more common to **not** include the comma; for example, I *bought potatoes, tomatoes, beans and sprouts,* rather than I *bought potatoes, tomatoes, beans, and sprouts.* However, it is acceptable in cases where there may be ambiguity or a need for clarification; for example, I *dedicate this book to Mum and Dad, Kate Mara and Iron Man.* Since it is unlikely the writer really means 'Mum and Dad' are Kate Mara and Iron Man, it can be rewritten as I *dedicate this book to Mum and Dad, Kate Mara, and Iron Man.*

Introduction

- Read the text with or to the class.
- Ask pupils to identify the text type and discuss the features of narrative text.
- Discuss the punctuation used.
- Discuss how difficult it would be to read without punctuation.

Full Stops – Page 66

- Read and discuss the definition of full stops.
- Work with those requiring additional assistance while the remainder of the class work independently on the activities.

Capital Letters – Page 67

- Read and discuss the information about the use of capital letters.
- Revise the definition of a sentence with pupils.
- Read with the class the statement about proper nouns. Ask for further examples and list them on the board.
- Emphasise that a capital letter is needed for names; hence 'my uncle' but 'Uncle Harry'.
- Explain that mum and dad only need a capital letter when used instead of their names; for example, *My mum and dad love animals – I asked Mum and Dad if I could have a pet.*
- Work with those requiring additional assistance while the remainder of the class work independently on the activities.

Commas – Page 68

- Read the information at the top of the page.
- Provide opportunities for pupils to read aloud and discuss in pairs their answers in Question 2. Reading aloud will provide the natural pauses indicating the need for a comma.
- Work with those requiring additional assistance while the remainder of the class work independently on the activities.

Direct Speech – Page 69

- Discuss the information given about direct speech.
- Emphasise that it is the *actual words* used. Elicit further examples.
- Examine and discuss with the class the placement of punctuation in the example given. Ask *why* the punctuation is placed where it is.
- Work with those requiring additional assistance while the remainder of the class work independently on the activities.

UNIT 10 FULL STOPS, CAPITAL LETTERS, COMMAS, DIRECT SPEECH

ANSWERS

Full Stops – Page 66

1. (b) and (c) need a full stop.

2. (a) The three pigs were brothers. They all left home and built themselves houses.
   (b) Sitting on the roof was a wolf. He called down the chimney to them.
   (c) One of the pigs suggested they write the wolf a letter. He might then just go away.

Capital Letters – Page 67

1. (a) ✗, ✗
   (b) ✓, ✓
   (c) ✓, ✓

2. (a) The pigs, whose names were Bob, Bill and Ben, lived in Port Piglet.
   (b) The wolf, who had been on the roof, bought a hamburger at Wolf Shopping Centre.
   (c) Wally Wolf had a hamburger for dinner on Thursday night.
   (d) He lived with his family at 10 Wolf Street in Pigston Village.

3. Teacher check

Commas – Page 68

1. (a) Dad enjoys playing golf, cricket and squash.
   (b) My sister has two cats, a dog, ten mice and a guinea pig.
   (c) I enjoy tennis, cricket, diving and swimming in the summer.

2. Teacher check

Direct Speech – Page 69

1. (a) Yes
   (b) No
   (c) No
   (d) Yes
   (e) Yes

2. (a) ✗
   (b) ✓
   (c) ✓
   (d) ✗

3. (a) 'Let's get some water', said one pig.
       'Let's get some water,' said one pig.
   (b) 'I don't think that is a good idea', thought his brother.
       'I don't think that is a good idea,' thought his brother.
   (c) 'I want to call the fire station', said the next pig.
       'I want to call the fire station,' said the next pig.
   (d) 'I'm off to buy a hamburger', said the wolf.
       'I'm off to buy a hamburger,' said the wolf.

Assessment Activity – Page 83

1. (a) blank (b) full stop (c) blank (d) full stop

2. (a) The wolf was on the roof. He was hoping to have dinner soon.
   (b) He had been sitting there for ages. He thought the pigs were very annoying.

3. A firefighter had rescued Mrs Walker's little kitten on Saturday.

4. The pigs had built houses out of straw, sticks and bricks.

5. (a) No
   (e) Yes

6. (a) 'Let me in!' the wolf shouted down the chimney.
   (b) 'I'm hungry and I want some pig for my dinner', he added.
       'I'm hungry and I want some pig for my dinner,' he added.

Class Record Sheet – Page viii

ASSESSMENT WRITING

- **Paragraph Topic** – *A Letter to a Wolf*
- **Focus: Punctuation** – *full stops, capital letters, commas, direct speech*

Self-evaluation – Page xiii

What Should We Do?

1. Three little pigs were sitting together in a brick house. There was a large, angry wolf on their roof calling down the chimney to them. The pigs were so concerned about this very dangerous situation that they decided to have a family conference to discuss their choices.

2. 'Well, we could put a pot of boiling water in the fireplace and hope he comes down the chimney and falls into it', suggested one of the pigs.

3. 'Or we could write him a letter and ask him to leave us alone. Could we say that we're really fed up with running away from him?' asked one of his brothers.

4. 'Or we could call for help. Perhaps if we phoned the fire station they would send someone out to remove him from our roof. I know they were very helpful last Saturday when Mrs Walker's kitten was stuck up a tree. I'm sure they would be happy to help us too', added the other brother.

5. The pigs were so busy sitting quietly, discussing their choices, that no one had answered the wolf on the roof. He waited and waited. Finally, he decided that the pigs must have all left the house. He hadn't heard a sound from any of them. So he left.

6. On his way home, he stopped and bought himself a tasty hamburger.

7. And ... they all lived happily ever after.

> A **full stop** (.) is used to show the end of a sentence.

---

1. **Put a full stop in the box if it is a complete sentence. Leave it blank if it is not.**

(a) The pigs had such quiet voices that ☐

(b) One pig wanted to boil him in a pot ☐

(c) Leave us alone ☐

2. **Put full stops where needed.**

(a) The three pigs were brothers They all left home and built themselves houses

(b) Sitting on the roof was a wolf He called down the chimney to them

(c) One of the pigs suggested they write the wolf a letter He might then just go away

CAPITAL LETTERS

A **capital letter** is used to start a sentence.

1. Is it a sentence? Is a capital letter needed? Put a ✓ or ✗ in the boxes.

(a) *waiting there on the roof*   It is a sentence. ☐   It needs a capital. ☐

(b) *would a firefighter come and help him?*   It is a sentence. ☐   It needs a capital. ☐

(c) *the pigs had a serious problem*   It is a sentence. ☐   It needs a capital. ☐

Proper nouns are the names of people, places or things. They need a capital letter; for example, Peter Pig, Pigston Village, Port Piglet.

2. Rewrite the sentence using a capital letter for proper nouns.

(a) The pigs, whose names were bob, bill and ben, lived in port piglet.

_____

_____

(b) The wolf, who had been on the roof, bought a hamburger at wolf shopping centre.

_____

_____

(c) Wally wolf had a hamburger for dinner on thursday night.

_____

_____

(d) He lived with his family at 10 wolf street in pigston village.

_____

_____

3. Write your

(a) name: _____

(b) address: _____

PUNCTUATION – COMMAS

A comma is used to separate things in a list; for example, 'I love cooking, sewing, reading and eating'. There is no comma before 'and'.

1. Rewrite the sentence, putting in commas where needed.

(a) Dad enjoys playing golf cricket and squash.

_____

_____

(b) My sister has two cats a dog ten mice and a guinea pig.

_____

(c) I enjoy tennis cricket diving and swimming in the summer.

_____

2. Write a list of:

(a) sports you like to play or watch

I enjoy watching or playing _____

_____

(b) people you would like to meet

I would like to meet _____

_____

(c) interesting places you have been

I have been to _____

_____

(d) places or countries you would like to visit

I would like to see _____

_____

When we write about people speaking, the words they say need speech marks. The speech marks are like two little hands around the words they say.

1. One pig said,
   'Let's get a pot of water'.

2. Another pig said,
   'Let's write a letter'.

3. The other pig said,
   'Let's phone for help'.

1. Read Paragraph 3. Tick yes or no.

(a) Are there any speech marks?   Yes ☐ No ☐

(b) Is the wolf speaking?   Yes ☐ No ☐

(c) Are two of the pigs speaking in this paragraph?   Yes ☐ No ☐

(d) Is there a capital letter at the start of the speech?   Yes ☐ No ☐

(e) Is there a question mark at the end of the speech?   Yes ☐ No ☐

2. Put a tick in the box if the sentence needs speech marks and a cross if it doesn't.

(a) The pig asked his brothers if they could tell the wolf they were fed up. ☐

(b) Then his brother said, We could phone the fire station.   ☐

(c) I'm sure they would help us too, he added.   ☐

(d) The wolf thought they had left.   ☐

3. Put speech marks around the correct words.

(a) Let's get some water, said one pig.

(b) I don't think that is a good idea, thought his brother.

(c) I want to call the fire station, said the next pig.

(d) I'm off to buy a hamburger said the wolf.

UNIT 11 — APOSTROPHES IN CONTRACTIONS

Focus

Punctuation – apostrophes in contractions

Progression

Recognise

Pupils will recognise apostrophes in contractions in modelled examples.

Choose

Pupils will write contractions correctly, with teacher support.

Use

Pupils will write contractions correctly in supplied and self-written sentences.

Definition of Terms

Contractions are new words made by joining two words and leaving out some letters.

Apostrophes are punctuation marks used to show where letters are missing in contractions. They are also used to show possession.

Introduction

Good writers improve their writing by using apostrophes correctly.

Teacher Information

Punctuation enables a writer to more fully and accurately communicate with the reader

Contractions in most cases only present difficulty for writers, the exception being *could've*, *would've* and *should've* which are often pronounced as though followed by 'of' instead of 'have'.

LESSON NOTES AND PLANS

Introduction

- Discuss apostrophes—what they are, where they are placed and why they are used; i.e. in contractions and to indicate possession.
- Explain that the focus in this section will be on apostrophes in contractions, and give some examples.
- Explain that contractions are quicker and easier to say, and discuss and model a variety of examples.

Apostrophes in Contractions – Page 72

- Read and discuss the definitions at the top of the page.
- Read the speech bubbles with the class and discuss why contractions are used in speech.
- Work through the activities with the class, ensuring they understand what is required of them.

Using Contractions – Page 73

- Pupils will be required to use 'not' in the contractions on this page.
- Remind them that it is important to put an apostrophe in the correct place and ask which letters of the word 'not' are usually left out.
- Give some examples of contractions with 'not' and discuss where the apostrophe is placed. (A common error is did'nt.)
- Provide opportunities for pupils to practise pronouncing the contractions correctly.
- Most pupils should be able to complete the page independently.

Don't and Won't – Page 74

- Read the speech bubbles on the page.
- Discuss pupils' answers to Question 1.
- Pupils can share the sentences they wrote in Question 4.
- Work through the activities with the class, ensuring they understand what is required of them.

Would, Could, Should and Must Have, It's or Its? – Page 75

- Discuss why using the word 'of' after would, could, should and must is always incorrect and reasons why this is a problem for speakers more than writers. (i.e. the 've' of 'have' sounds like the 'v' of the word 'of').
- Discuss the use of 'its' and 'it's' with pupils. Explain the difference and use of each.
- Emphasise that it's easy to work out which to use by asking the simple question, *'Can I say "it is" here?'* If the answer is 'yes', an apostrophe is needed. Note: *It has* is also contracted to *it's*.
- Work through the activities with the class, ensuring they understand what is required of them.

UNIT 11   APOSTROPHES IN CONTRACTIONS

ANSWERS

Apostrophes in Contractions – Page 72

1. (a) I would like to swim with dolphins.
(b) Let us try and take some photos.
(c) We have already been to see the seals.
(d) They will be late unless they hurry.

2. Teacher check

3. (a) he's
(b) you're
(c) they're
(d) we're
(e) I'm
(f) you've
(g) she'll
(h) they've

Using Contractions – Page 73

1. (a) He's been wanting to see some dolphins.
(b) She's so excited about it too.
(c) He's running towards the dolphin pool.
(d) She's brought her mobile phone to take photos.

2. (a) must not
(b) had not
(c) did not
(d) could not
(e) would not
(f) can not

3. Teacher check

4. (a) you'd
(b) you're
(c) you'd
(d) you'll
(e) can't
(f) you've

Don't and Won't – Page 74

1. (a) Don't swim in the pool.
(b) Don't forget the sunscreen
(c) Don't walk so slowly.
(d) Don't run so fast.

2. Teacher check

3. (a) 4
(b) i, l, l
(c) o and n
(d) w and t

4. Teacher check

Would, Could, Should and Must Have, It's or Its? – Page 75

1. (a) I would have been late.
(b) We must have forgotten.
(c) He could have run faster.
(d) They should have hurried.

2. (a) We should've caught the bus.
(b) He should've left the pool earlier.
(c) He could've run much faster
(d) They all should've hurried.

3. (a) it's
(b) it and is (or has)

4. (a) its
(b) it's
(c) it's
(d) it's

5. Teacher check

Assessment Activity – Page 84

1. (a) We will
(b) You are
(c) They will

2. (a) I don't know where your hat is.
(b) Perhaps it's in your bag.
(c) You'll have to look for it.

3. (a) didn't
(b) they've
(c) he'll
(d) we're

4. Teacher check

5. (a) will not (b) Teacher check

6. (a) it's, it's
(b) its, its
(c) Teacher check

7. Teacher check–must've

Class Record Sheet – Page viii

ASSESSMENT WRITING

• **Paragraph Topic** – *Don't Do It!*

• **Focus: Punctuation** – *Apostrophes in Contractions*

Self-evaluation – Page xiii

APOSTROPHES IN CONTRACTIONS

> **Contractions** are new words made by joining words, usually two, and leaving out some of their letters. An apostrophe is used in a contraction to show that some letters are missing.

1. Write the sentence using two words instead of the contraction.

   (a) I'd like to swim with dolphins.

   _____

   _____

   (b) Let's try and take some photos.

   _____

   _____

   (c) We've already been to see the seals.

   _____

   _____

   (d) They'll be late unless they hurry.

   _____

2. Use the contraction in a sentence.

   (a) We'd _____

   (b) She'll _____

   (c) He is _____

3. Join the two words to make a contraction. Don't forget the apostrophe.

   (a) he is _____   (b) you are _____

   (c) they are _____   (d) we are _____

   (e) I am _____   (f) you have _____

   (g) she will _____   (h) they have _____

USING CONTRACTIONS

1. Write the sentence using a contraction.

(a) He has been wanting to see some dolphins.

_____

(b) She is so excited about it too.

_____

(c) He is running towards the dolphin pool.

_____

(d) She has brought her mobile phone to take photos.

_____

2. Write the two words for each contraction.

(a) mustn't _____   (b) hadn't _____

(c) didn't _____   (d) couldn't _____

(e) wouldn't _____   (f) can't _____

3. Write a sentence using the contraction.

(a) mustn't _____

_____

(b) couldn't _____

_____

(c) shouldn't _____

_____

4. Write the contractions.

(a) you had _____   (b) you are _____

(c) you would _____   (d) you will _____

(e) can not _____   (f) you have _____

DON'T AND WON'T

1. Change *do not* to *don't* and complete the sentence.

Do not swim in the pool.

(a) The park attendant said, '_____ in the pool'.

Do not forget the sunscreen.

(b) Mum said, '_____ the sunscreen'.

Do not walk so slowly.

(c) Sam said, '_____ so slowly'.

Do not run so fast.

(d) Jane said, '_____ so fast'.

2. Write a sentence your teacher might say to you using 'don't'.

_____

_____

will not won't	Don't you think this contraction is strange?

3. (a) How many letters from the two joined words are in the contraction? _____

(b) Which letters are not in the contraction? _____

(c) Which two letters change places? _____

(d) Which two letters stay in the same places? _____

4. Complete the sentence using 'won't'.

(a) I _____

(b) The children _____

WOULD, COULD, SHOULD AND MUST HAVE, IT'S OR ITS?

1. Never, never say this! Correct these terrible mistakes.

(a) I would of been late. _____

(b) We must of forgotten. _____

(c) He could of run faster. _____

(d) They should of hurried. _____

2. Write the sentence using a contraction.

(a) We should have caught the bus.

_____

(b) He should have left the pool earlier.

_____

(c) He could have run much faster.

_____

(d) They all should have hurried.

_____

> ## Its or it's
> These two little words cause lots of trouble for writers.
> Only one of them is a contraction.

3. (a) Which one is the contraction? _____

(b) It is a contraction of _____ and _____ .

4. Circle **'its'** or **'it's'**. HINT: Only use **'it's'** if you can say **'it is'** instead of **'it's'**.

(a) The dog lost its / it's bone.   (b) I think its / it's buried in the garden.

(c) I wonder if its / it's near the fence.   (d) I know its / it's somewhere near here.

5. Write a sentence using:

(a) it's _____

(b) its _____

UNIT 12   APOSTROPHES FOR POSSESSION

Focus

Punctuation – apostrophes for possesion

Progression

Recognise

Pupils will recognise possessive apostrophes in modelled examples.

Choose

Pupils will choose appropriate possessive apostrophes for sentences with teacher support.

Use

Pupils will correctly use possessive apostrophes in supplied and self-written sentences.

Definition of Terms

A **possessive apostrophe** is a punctuation mark used to show ownership.

Introduction

Good writers improve their writing by using apostrophes correctly.

Teacher Information

Punctuation enables a writer to more fully and accurately communicate with the reader.

Possessive apostrophes show who or what possesses the noun referred to; for example, *The man's hand*.

Introduction

- Discuss different ways of saying that something belongs to someone.
- Point to different objects in the classroom and ask 'Who owns this?' Encourage answers such as 'It is Cate's desk'. Write an example on the board and ask what the apostrophe is called.
- Explain that an apostrophe is the quickest way of expressing ownership and that this is not possible in many other languages.

Apostrophes for Ownership – Page 78

- Read the information and the rule for using apostrophes.
- Work through the page with pupils.
- Work with those requiring additional assistance while the remainder of the class work independently on the activities.

Who Owns What? – Page 79

- Read the rule at the top of the page.
- Revise how ownership can be deduced from the placement of the apostrophe and where its 'tail' is pointing.
- Work through the first question as a group, with teacher support, to ensure understanding.
- Work with those requiring additional assistance while the remainder of the class work independently on the activities.

How Many Owners? – Page 80

- Read the information at the top of the page.
- Work through the steps and the example with the class.
- Work through Question 1 with pupils, providing support or additional information where needed.
- Continue to work with those requiring additional assistance while the remainder of the class work independently on the activities.

Practise Using Apostrophes – Page 81

- Read and discuss the rule about 's' at the top of the page.
- Work through the examples with the class.
- Explain that in Question 1 the owners all end with 's' so there is no need to add one.
- Pupils can then complete the activity.
- In Question 2 the owners do not end with 's' so one will need to be added.
- Revise the concept of ownership as a pair; for example, *Jack and Jill's hill*, and the placement of the apostrophe.
- Allow pupils to work through the exercises, assisting as required.

UNIT 12 APOSTROPHES FOR POSSESSION

ANSWERS

Apostrophes for Ownership – Page 78

1. (a) the hippo
   (b) hippo
   (c) Yes
   (d) Yes

2. (a) Crocodiles
   (b) the crocodiles
   (c) Yes
   (d) Yes

3. Teacher check

Who Owns What? – Page 79

1. (a) the shark
   (b) the whales

2. (a) a seal ✓
   (b) the crabs ✓
   (c) a fisherman ✓
   (d) those seagulls ✓
   (e) my father✓

3. (a) a shark's teeth
   (b) the fish's scales
   (c) the water's edge
   (d) the beach's sand

4. Teacher check

How Many Owners? – Page 80

1. (a) the lion – one owner
   (b) the rabbits – more than one owner
   (c) the zebras – more than one owner
   (d) the fox – one owner
   (e) the monkey – one owner

Practise Using Apostrophes – Page 81

1. (a) dogs'
   (b) girls'
   (c) ducks'
   (d) bees'

2. (a) school's
   (b) shop's
   (c) cow's
   (d) baker's

3. (a) John and Ben's mother
   (b) Oliver and Ben's hats
   (c) Zoe and Ben's school

4. Teacher check

Assessment Activity – Page 85

1. after

2. (a) Jan and Zoe
   (b) his shirts
   (c) the man
   (d) the shops

3. (a) the coach – one owner
   (b) their teachers – more than one owner
   (c) Bill and Ben – more than one owner

4. (a) girls'
   (b) men's
   (c) boys'

5. Teacher check

Class Record Sheet – Page viii

ASSESSMENT WRITING

• **Paragraph Topic** – *A Beautiful Beach*
• **Focus: Punctuation** – *Apostrophes for Possession*

Self-evaluation – Page xiii

APOSTROPHES FOR OWNERSHIP

Follow the Rules

There are many rules to tell us what we can and can't do in a park. There are rules for writers too. This one tells where to put an apostrophe to show someone owns something.

RULE: An apostrophe is placed after the owner or the owners.

Does this sentence follow the rule?   *This is the hippo's pool.*

1. (a) Who is the owner?_____

   (b) Which word is the apostrophe after? _____

   (c) Does this apostrophe follow the rule?   Yes ☐   No ☐

   (d) Does the tail of the apostrophe point to the owner?   Yes ☐   No ☐

2. Check if this sentence follows the rule.   *Crocodiles' jaws are very strong.*

   (a) Which word is the apostrophe after? _____

   (b) Who owns the jaws? _____

   (c) Does this apostrophe follow the rule?   Yes ☐   No ☐

   (d) Does the tail of the apostrophe point to the owners?   Yes ☐   No ☐

3. Write a sentence using:

   (a) the monkeys' cage

   _____

   _____

   (b) the elephant's trunk

   _____

   _____

WHO OWNS WHAT?

> **RULE:** An apostrophe is placed after the owner or the owners.

1. Use the rule. It will help you to find and write the name of the owner or owners.

   (a) the shark's fins _____

   (b) the whales' small eyes _____

2. Write the name of the owner/s.
Put a tick or cross to show if it follows the rule.

   (a) a seal's pup   _____ ☐

   (b) the crabs' claws   _____ ☐

   (c) a fisherman's boat   _____ ☐

   (d) those seagulls' wings   _____ ☐

   (e) my father's fishing rod _____ ☐

3. Who owns what? Use 's' and an apostrophe to show the owner.

   water   shark   fish   beach

   (a) a _____ teeth

   (b) the _____ scales

   (c) the _____ edge

   (d) the _____ sand

4. (a) Draw a picture of something
you wish you owned.

   (b) Write your name and use an
apostrophe to tell who you are
and what you wish you owned.

   If wishes come true this will be _____.

   (c) Write a sentence about something you own. Start with your name and an
apostrophe.

   _____

   _____

HOW MANY OWNERS?

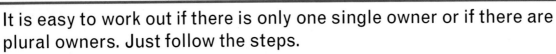

It is easy to work out if there is only one single owner or if there are plural owners. Just follow the steps.

Step 1   Find the apostrophe.

Step 2   Find the owner. (What is written just before the apostrophe?)

Step 3   Ask yourself if there is one or more than one of them.

The children's party was at the zoo.

Let's follow the steps to find out if there is one or more owners.

Step 1   Read it, find the apostrophe and put a circle around it.

Step 2   Find the owner or owners, underline and write on the line.

Step 3   Ask yourself if there is one or more owners. Tick one box.

one owner ☐   more than one owner ☑

---

1. Follow the three steps.

- Circle the apostrophe.

- Underline and write the owner/owners.

- Tick one box.

(a) the lion's mane

owner/owners _____

one owner ☐   more than one owner ☐

(b) the rabbits' burrow

owner/owners _____

one owner ☐   more than one owner ☐

(c) the zebras' stripes

owner/owners _____

one owner ☐   more than one owner ☐

(d) the fox's den

owner/owners _____

one owner ☐   more than one owner ☐

(e) the monkey's tricks

owner/owners _____

one owner ☐   more than one owner ☐

TEACHING WRITING STRATEGIES (Book 3)
www.prim-ed.com

978-1-912760-36-7

PRACTISE USING APOSTROPHES

> **RULE:** There must be an 's' before or after the apostrophe showing ownership.

If the owner or owners do not have an 's' at the end it has to be added.

- The cage that belongs to the lion is the lion's cage.
- The cage that belongs to the tiger is the tiger's cage.

If the owners have an 's' at the end there is no need to add one.

- The shoes that belong to the ladies are the ladies' shoes.
- The shoes that belong to the horses are the horses' shoes.

1. Add an apostrophe to show ownership. The owners all end with 's' so don't add one.

   (a) The collars belong to the dogs. They are the _____ collars.

   (b) The dolls belong to the girls. They are the _____ dolls.

   (c) The ducklings belong to the ducks. They are the _____ ducklings.

   (d) The hive belongs to the bees. It is the _____ hive.

2. Add an apostrophe to show ownership. The owners do not end with 's' so add an 's'.

   (a) The gate belongs to our school. It is our _____ gate.

   (b) The cakes belong to the shop. They are the _____ cakes.

   (c) The calves belong to this cow. They are this _____ calves.

   (d) The bread belongs to the baker. It is the _____ bread.

> **RULE:** When there are two names only one name has an apostrophe.
> • Ben and John's mother • Ben and Oliver's hats • Ben and Zoe's school

3. Change the word order so Ben's name has an apostrophe and his friends don't.

   (a) Ben and John's mother _____

   (b) Ben and Oliver's hats _____

   (c) Ben and Zoe's school _____

4. Write a sentence about something you and someone else own. Start with both your names.

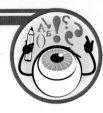

Name: _____ Date: _____

there is a boat at Niagara called maid of the mist. It takes you up close to the falls it's quite scary and the noise is so loud there that you can't hear anything else It's amazing! they gave us raincoats to wear, but we were soaking wet when we finished the trip.

1. (a) Use a red pen or pencil to add the missing capital letters and full stops.

(b) How many capital letters did you need? _____

(c) How many capital letters did you need for proper nouns? _____

(d) How many full stops did you add? _____

2. Write a proper noun that tells you:

(a) your country _____

(b) your doctor's name _____

(c) the name of your school _____

3. Write a sentence with a proper noun.

_____

4. Put a tick in the box if the punctuation is correct.

(a) Help me? ☐　　(b) Wait at the gate. ☐　　(c) why did you do that? ☐

(d) Mix butter and sugar! ☐　　(e) How did he do that? ☐　　(f) Don't fall! ☐

5. Write the sentence with a question mark, full stop or exclamation mark.

(a) What did you see there _____

(b) We were soaking wet _____

(c) Hold on _____

(d) Put on this coat _____

6. Put a tick in the box if the punctuation is correct.

(a) Professor Simons ☐　(b) Sleeping beauty ☐　(c) my favourite book ☐

(d) the Eiffel tower ☐　(e) Tower of London ☐　(f) river amazon ☐

FULL STOPS, CAPITAL LETTERS, COMMAS, DIRECT SPEECH

Name: _____ Date: _____

1. Put a full stop in the box after a complete sentence. Leave it blank otherwise.

(a) discussing what to do ☐   (b) The pigs couldn't make a decision ☐

(c) The wolf just ☐   (d) The hamburger was good ☐

2. Add full stops where needed.

(a) The wolf was on the roof He was hoping to have dinner soon

(b) He had been sitting there for ages He thought the pigs were very annoying

3. Rewrite the sentence. Put capital letters where needed.

A firefighter had rescued mrs walker's little kitten on saturday.

_____

_____

4. Rewrite the sentence. Put commas where needed.

The pigs had built houses out of straw sticks and bricks.

_____

_____

5. Does the sentence need quotation marks?

(a) One of the pigs said he would write a letter.   Yes ☐ No ☐

(b) What should we do? they asked   Yes ☐ No ☐

6. Rewrite the sentence. Add quotation marks where needed.

(a) Let me in! the wolf shouted down the chimney.

_____

_____

(b) I'm hungry and I want some pig for my dinner, he added.

_____

_____

Name: _____ Date: _____

1. Circle the contractions. Write them as two words.

(a) We'll need warm clothes. _____

(b) You're not wearing shorts. _____

(c) They'll not keep you warm. _____

2. Rewrite the sentences using contractions.

(a) I do not know where your hat is. _____

(b) Perhaps it is in your bag. _____

(c) You will have to look for it. _____

3. Join the two words to make a contraction. Don't forget to use an apostrophe.

(a) did not _____ (b) they have _____

(c) he will _____ (d) we are _____

4. Write a sentence using 'don't'.

_____

5. (a) Which two words are joined to make the contraction 'won't'?

_____ _____

(b) Write a sentence using 'won't'.

_____

6. Circle the correct words.

(a) I think it's/its going to be cold, but of course, it's/its winter.

(b) That dog wearing it's/its warm coat is wagging it's/its tail.

(c) Write you own sentence using 'its'.

_____

7. Use the contraction of 'must have' in a sentence.

_____

Name: _____ Date: _____

1. Complete the rule:

An apostrophe is placed _____ the owner or owners.

2. Write the name of the owner or owners.

(a) Jan and Zoe's dresses _____ (b) his shirts' collar _____

(c) the man's coat _____ (d) the shops' windows _____

3. Follow the three steps.
- Circle the apostrophe.
- Underline and write the owner/owners.
- Tick one box.

(a) the coach's whistle   owner/owners _____
one owner ☐   more than one owner ☐

(b) their teachers' cars   owner/owners _____
one owner ☐   more than one owner ☐

(c) Bill and Ben's vegetables   owner/owners _____
one owner ☐   more than one owner ☐

4. Add an apostrophe to show ownership.

(a) The jeans belong to the girls.   They are the _____ jeans.

(b) The ties belong to the men.   They are the _____ ties.

(c) The shirts belongs to the boys. They are the _____ shirts.

5. (a) Write the name of your sister, brother or friend. _____

(b) What is something he or she owns? _____

(c) It is _____.

(d) Write a sentence about something you and he/she own.
Start with both your names.

_____

_____

UNIT 13   SPELLING (VOWEL SOUNDS), SENTENCE STRUCTURE, PUNCTUATION, WORD CHOICES, EDITING

Focus

Editing and proofreading – spelling (vowel sounds), sentence structure, punctuation, word choices, editing

Progression

Recognise

When editing and proofreading their writing, pupils will recognise correct and appropriate spelling, punctuation, word choices and sentence structure.

Choose

When editing and proofreading their writing, pupils will choose correct and appropriate spelling, punctuation, word choices and sentence structure.

Use

When editing and proofreading their writing, pupils will use correct and appropriate spelling, punctuation, word choices and sentence structure.

Definition of Terms

A **vowel** is a principal speech sound.

Introduction

Good writers improve their writing by using correct spelling and punctuation and by choosing appropriate vocabulary, word choices and sentence structure.

Teacher Information

Knowledge of vowel sound graphemes enables a writer to make informed choices in spelling.

Introduction

- Discuss the purpose of editing and proofreading writing and how it is an essential part of the writing process.

Vowel Sounds – Page 88

- Discuss the vowels and the different ways in which they are represented in words. Provide examples of words with different graphemes representing the long 'a' sound – tr**ay**, tr**ai**n, th**ey**, fl**a**me and long 'e' – tr**ee**, m**e**, l**ea**f, th**e**se.
- Work with the class to brainstorm words with long 'e' vowel sounds.
- List these on the board. Retain.
- Elicit from pupils the graphemes that represent the vowel sound in each word and sort them into grapheme groups.
- The long 'i', 'o' and 'u' sounds can then be discussed in a similar way.
- Work as a class through Question 1(a).
- What word do they think is spelled incorrectly?
- What is the vowel sound?
- What other graphemes represent that sound (refer to groups on board)? Correct the misspelled word.
- Work with those requiring additional assistance while the remainder of the class work independently on the activities.

Sentence Structure and Punctuation – Page 89

- Read the information at the top of the page.
- Elicit some examples of complete and incomplete sentences from pupils. Write them on the board.
- Emphasise that a sentence makes sense by itself.
- Read the text and work through the questions with pupils, providing support or additional information where needed.
- Continue to work with those requiring additional assistance while the remainder of the class work independently on the activities.

Word Choices – Page 90

- Read the information at the top of the page.
- Revise the importance of word choice when writing; for example, verb forms, tenses, adverbs, adjectives, I or me, boring (pallid) verbs (got, said, went etc.).
- Allow pupils to work through the exercises, assisting as required.

Edited Text – Page 91

- Read the information at the top of the page. Emphasise the checking aspect.
- As a class, discuss the basic reasons for editing and proofreading; i.e. *to make it correct; to make it better*.
- Allow pupils time to read the text before commencing the activities.
- Discuss any problems that may arise at this time.
- Pupils work independently or with assistance on the activities.

UNIT 13 SPELLING (VOWEL SOUNDS), SENTENCE STRUCTURE, PUNCTUATION, WORD CHOICES, EDITING

ANSWERS

Vowel Sounds – Page 88

1. (a) great
   (b) waves
   (c) straight
   (d) happy
   (e) journey
   (f) waterski
   (g) island
   (h) high
   (i) butterfly
   (j) over
   (k) rainbow
   (l) toes
   (m) through
   (n) rule
   (o) pool

2. (a) ✘
   (b) ✘
   (c) ✓
   (d) ✘
   (e) ✘

Sentence Structure and Punctuation – Page 89

1. (a) Yes (in)
   (b) Yes (one)

2. (a) No, a full stop after 'world', a capital for 'they' and 'shark'.
   (b) Yes, No, Australia

3. (a) 6
   (b) Teacher check. Possible answer: I wouldn't like to see one near me because I think they're frightening.
   (c) 3, Teacher check. Possible answer: They are huge, aggressive and dangerous.

Word Choices – Page 90

1. (a) did
   (b) done
   (c) did
   (d) went
   (e) caught
   (f) will cook
   (g) I
   (h) me
   (i) me

2. (a)–(c) Teacher check
   (d) him
   (e) they
   (f) who

3. Teacher check

Edited Text – Page 91

1. (a) He
   (b) Yes, reduces repetition and improves flow.

2. Captain Ahab became tangled in the ropes. He was drowned.

3. (a) False
   (b)–(c) Teacher check

4. will be – was, wrong tense

5. captain, drowned

6. grate – great

Assessment Activity – Page 110

1. (a) straight
   (b) happy
   (c) high
   (d) through
   (e) over

2. We climbed out of the pool because we were cold.

3. Our family travelled to Green Island by boat. It was a long trip but we had fun. On the way back, we saw dolphins.

4. (a) did (b) done

5.–8. Teacher check

Class Record Sheet – Page ix

ASSESSMENT WRITING

- **Paragraph Topic** – *Sharks*
- **Focus: Editing and Proofreading** – *spelling (vowel sounds), sentence structure, punctuation, word choices, editing*

Self-evaluation– Page xiii

VOWEL SOUNDS

> Good writers check their spelling. They check that they have chosen the correct vowel sounds for the words they have used.

Underline the word spelled incorrectly. Write it correctly at the end of the line.

1. (a) It think it's grait to go to the beach in summer. _____

(b) I love to splash in the wayvs. _____

(c) If I spot a large one coming I dive strayt under. _____

(d) Sometimes my dad is happey to take us to the lake. _____

(e) It is a long journee but we enjoy the trip. _____

(f) At the lake, I have learnt to waterskey. _____

(g) Last holidays, our family toured an eisland. _____

(h) The gulls flew hy all around the rocks. _____

(i) One afternoon, we spotted a beautiful butterfligh. _____

(j) Near our beach house is a waterfall oaver the rocks. _____

(k) When it has been raining, we often see a rainboe. _____

(l) The water feels really cold on my tose when I paddle. _____

(m) At Nan's farm we walk threw the bush to the river. _____

(n) Dad has a rool that we shouldn't go there alone. _____

(o) He thinks it could be too dangerous near the large pule. _____

2. Put a tick or a cross in the box to show if the vowel sound in the 'w' word is correct.

(a) Without worning, the rain started. ☐

(b) It was the werst storm for many months. ☐

(c) Earlier in the morning, the weather had been warm. ☐

(d) We wondered whot damage had been done. ☐

(e) The thunder was so loud it was difficult to hear the wards we spoke. ☐

SENTENCE STRUCTURE AND PUNCTUATION

> Good writers check their sentences make sense and that the punctuation is correct.

You will need a red pen or pencil to make corrections and changes to the text.

Sharks swim fast and have many very sharp teeth. they are found in oceans around the world shark attacks at popular swimming beaches in australia have made them one one of the most feared creatures found the sea.

1. **Check the sentences.**

(a) Are there any words missing? _____ If so, add them.

(b) Are there extra words that are not needed? _____ If so, cross them out.

2. **Check the punctuation.**

(a) Do the sentences all start with capital letters and end with full stops?

_____ If not, add them.

(b) Are there any proper nouns? _____ Do they start with capital letters?

_____ If not, add them.

> Good writers join sentences to make their writing better.

Great whites are one of the most feared sharks. They are huge. They are aggressive. They are dangerous. I wouldn't like to see one near me. I think they're frightening.

3. (a) How many complete sentences are there? _____

(b) Show how you could join the last two sentences.
Write your new sentence.

_____

_____

(c) How many sentences start with 'they'? _____ Join them.

_____

_____

WORD CHOICES

| Good writers correct, change and add words to improve their writing. |

1. Correct the underlined word. Write it on the line.

(a) All the children <u>done</u> the work very well. _____

(b) Have you <u>did</u> the writing yet? _____

(c) The teachers all <u>done</u> the marking. _____

(d) Yesterday, I <u>will go</u> fishing with Dad. _____

(e) At the weekend, we <u>catched</u> lots of fish. _____

(f) Tonight, Mum <u>will cooking</u> them for our tea. _____

(g) My sister and <u>me</u> like playing in the waves at the beach. _____

(h) We chase each other and she splashes <u>I</u>. _____

(i) Would you like to come to the beach with my sister and <u>I</u>? _____

2. Choose a better word. Write it on the line.

(a) Our family <u>got</u> into our car to travel to the beach. _____

(b) When we arrived, we all <u>got</u> out our towels and swimsuits. _____

(c) After staying all day, we <u>got</u> home at seven o'clock. _____

(d) John came to the beach with us then Dad dropped <u>John</u> home. _____

(e) His parents were away for the weekend but <u>his parents</u> were home now.

_____

(f) We told John's parents about the man <u>that</u> came too. _____

3. Add words in the spaces to improve the sentences.

(a) The _____ waves were crashing onto the shore.

(b) While at the beach, our family sighted a _____ dolphin.

(c) The huge waterfall tumbled _____ down the hillside.

(d) Climbing _____ down to the shore we could hear the roar.

TEACHING WRITING STRATEGIES (Book 3)
www.prim-ed.com
978-1-912760-36-7

EDITED TEXT

> Good writers check their work carefully. They ask themselves:
> Is it right? How can I make it better?

Have you heard the story of 'Moby Dick'? ~~Moby Dick~~ *He* was a grate white whale that was hunted by the crew of a whaling ship long ~~ago.~~ The *captain* captan of the ship, Ahab, *false*, had a leg made of whalebone. He said the white whale had taken his real leg. The ship eventually found Moby Dick. Captain Ahab became tangled *was* *drowned* ~~in the ropes~~ and will be drownded.

1. (a) Which pronoun did the editor use in place of a name? _____

(b) Do you think this made the text better? _____ Why?

_____

2. Write the two ideas joined by the conjunction 'and' in the last sentence.

_____

_____

3. (a) Write the adjective the editor added to describe the leg. _____

(b) Add some adjectives to describe the white whale.
Which adjectives did you add?

_____

_____

(c) Do you think you made the text better? _____ Why?

_____

4. Find the verb the editor changed. Why was it changed?

_____

5. There are two spelling mistakes marked by the editor.

What are they? _____ and _____

6. The editor missed one spelling mistake.

What is it? _____ Correct it. _____

UNIT 14 | SPELLING (MORE VOWEL SOUNDS), SENTENCE STRUCTURE, PUNCTUATION, WORD CHOICES, EDITING

Focus

Editing and proofreading – spelling (vowel sounds), sentence structure, punctuation, word choices, editing

Progression

Recognise
When editing and proofreading their writing, pupils will recognise correct and appropriate spelling, punctuation, word choices and sentence structure.

Choose
When editing and proofreading their writing, pupils will choose correct and appropriate spelling, punctuation, word choices and sentence structure.

Use
When editing and proofreading their writing, pupils will use correct and appropriate spelling, punctuation, word choices and sentence structure.

Definition of Terms

A **vowel** is a principal speech sound.

Introduction

Good writers improve their writing by using correct spelling and punctuation and by choosing appropriate vocabulary, word choices and sentence structure.

Teacher Information

Knowledge of vowel sound graphemes enables a writer to make informed choices in spelling.

LESSON NOTES AND PLANS

Introduction

- Discuss the purpose of editing and proofreading writing and how it is an essential part of the writing process.

More Vowel Sounds – Page 94

- Revise vowel sounds and the different ways in which they are represented in words.
- Read the information at the top of the page.
- Work as a class through Question 1(a).
- What word do they think is spelled incorrectly?
- What is the vowel sound?
- What other graphemes represent that sound?
- Correct the misspelt word.
- Questions 4 and 5 focus on words that are often misspelt. Discuss with the class ways of remembering these words; for example, saying the word as it is spelled – Wed/nes/day or Feb/ru/ary.
- Work with those requiring additional assistance while the remainder of the class work independently on the activities.

Sentence Structure and Punctuation – Page 95

- Read the information at the top of the page.
- Elicit some examples of common punctuation types from pupils; for example, full stops, commas and capital letters. Write them on the board.
- Read the text and work through Question 1 with pupils, providing support or additional information where needed.
- Continue to work with those requiring additional assistance while the remainder of the class work independently on the activities.

Word Choices – Page 96

- Read the information at the top of the page.
- Revise the importance of word choice when writing; for example, tenses, adverbs, adjectives, I or me, boring (pallid) verbs (got, said, went etc.).
- Allow pupils to work through the exercises, assisting as required.

Edited Text – Page 97

- Read the information at the top of the page. Emphasise the checking aspect.
- As a class, discuss the basic reasons for editing and proofreading; i.e. *to make it correct; to make it better.*
- Allow pupils time to read the text before commencing the activities.
- Discuss any problems that may arise at this time.
- Pupils work independently or with assistance on the activities.

978-1-912760-36-7

UNIT 14 — SPELLING (MORE VOWEL SOUNDS), SENTENCE STRUCTURE, PUNCTUATION, WORD CHOICES, EDITING

More Vowel Sounds – Page 94

1. (a) pearl
   (b) earn
   (c) journeyed
   (d) country
   (e) discover
   (f) flood
   (g) wreck
   (h) climbed
   (i) calm

2. (a) something
   (b) difficult
   (c) because
   (d) favourite
   (e) special
   (f) dangerous
   (g) picture
   (h) beautiful

3. (a) Our class placed our lunches into the boxes ready to be taken to the bus.
   (b) The gardener grew potatoes, tomatoes and avocados which he sold at the market.

Sentence Structure and Punctuation – Page 95

1. (a) after 'claps'
   (b) after 'them' (first mention)
   (c) a question mark
   (d) Sealand Park

2. (a) dolphins
   (b) No. It doesn't show ownership and it's not a contraction.

3. (a) Sentence 1
   (b) It tells that the paragraph is about dolphins.

4. Teacher check. Possible answer: You can see its body before it lands with a splash and everyone claps.

Word Choices – Page 96

1. (a) seen
   (b) saw
   (c) seen
   (d) are
   (e) am
   (f) Are
   (g) it's
   (h) its
   (i) have
   (j) have

2. (a)–(c) Teacher check
   (d) who
   (e) that
   (f) were

3. Teacher check

Edited Text – Page 97

1. (a) 2
   (b) tentacles

2. (a) 'large' and 'colourful'
   (b) Yes

3. to

4. (a) 'isn't' to 'aren't'
   (b) The verb should be plural; subject–verb agreement.

5. to join sentences

6. a spelling/homophone error

7. statement, not a question

Assessment Activity – Page 111

1. (a) earn
   (b) country
   (c) write
   (d) climbed

2. (a) The books were packed into large boxes by the class.
   (b) I love to eat potatoes and tomatoes.

3. Teacher check

4. (a) saw
   (b) its

5. (a) full stop and question mark
   (b) Sentence 1
   (c) No
   (d) No – we've.
   (e) Teacher check. Possible answer: We enjoy seeing the animals, but we especially enjoy the horses.

Class Record Sheet – Page ix

ASSESSMENT WRITING

Paragraph Topic – *Dolphins*
Focus: Editing and Proofreading – *spelling (vowel sounds), sentence structure, punctuation, word choices, editing.*

Self-evaluation– Page xiii

UNIT 14
MORE VOWEL SOUNDS

Good writers check their spelling. They check that they have chosen the correct vowel sounds for the words they have used.

Underline the word spelled incorrectly. Write it correctly on the line.

1. (a) On the island were many purl farmers. _____

(b) They must work very hard to urn a living. _____

(c) We jearneyed down to the coast to watch them. _____

(d) One summer, our family rented a cottage in the cuontry. _____

(e) We toured around to discuver many interesting places. _____

(f) There had been a severe storm so one river was in floud. _____

(g) In the ocean nearby was an old reck. _____

(h) My brother and I climed over the rocks to get closer. _____

(i) When the sea was cam we could swim out to it. _____

2. Some words may be tricky to spell. See if you can unjumble these tricky words. Look at the first letter for a clue!

(a) thismeong   s_____   (b) ifclitufd   d_____

(c) sucaebe   b_____   (d) teavfouri   f_____

(e) pilasce   s_____   (f) gsudnareo   d_____

(g) ctpreui   p_____   (h) eatbifuul   b_____

3. Underline the three words spelled incorrectly. Rewrite the sentence.

(a) Our class placed our lunchs into the boxs ready to be taken to the buss.

_____

_____

(b) The gardener grew potatos, tomatos and avocadoes which he sold at the market.

_____

_____

_____

TEACHING WRITING STRATEGIES (Book 3)
www.prim-ed.com
978-1-912760-36-7

SENTENCE STRUCTURE AND PUNCTUATION

Good writers check their sentences and punctuation.

You will need a red pen or pencil to make corrections and changes to the text.

Do you like dolphin's? I love them They always seem such happy and playful creatures. Sometimes at sealand park one of them jumps up out of the water. You can see its body and then it lands with a splash and then everyone claps

1. (a) Find the missing full stop and add it. Put a circle around it.

(b) There is an exclamation mark missing. Add it and put a circle around it.

(c) What other punctuation was used at the end of a sentence?

_____

(d) There are two proper nouns. Correct them and write them on the line.

_____

2. (a) Find and write the word that has an apostrophe. _____

(b) Does it need an apostrophe? _____ Why/Why not?

_____

_____

Good writers start a paragraph by telling what it is about.

3. (a) Is Sentence 1 or Sentence 3 the better one to start the paragraph

with? _____

(b) Why?_____

4. (a) Underline the words 'and then' in Sentence 5.

(b) Rewrite this sentence without these words.

_____

_____

WORD CHOICES

Good writers correct, change and add words to improve their writing.

1. Correct the underlined word. Write it on the line.

(a) Have you <u>see</u> the fish swimming around the lake? _____

(b) My friend <u>seen</u> them yesterday. _____

(c) His sister had <u>saw</u> them as well. _____

(d) Where <u>is</u> you and your family going for their picnic? _____

(e) I <u>were</u> coming with them to the beach. _____

(f) <u>Is</u> you coming too? _____

(g) Tomorrow, <u>its</u> going to be a lovely day. _____

(h) We can visit the farm and see the horse and <u>it's</u> new foal. _____

(i) You could <u>of</u> seen the foal when you were there. _____

(j) It would <u>of</u> looked so cute. _____

2. Choose a better word. Write it on the line.

(a) The family <u>went</u> to the farm by car. _____

(b) Do you know which way they <u>went</u>? _____

(c) They <u>went</u> to look at the new foal. _____

(d) The farmer <u>that</u> owns the new foal looks after it well. _____

(e) The mare <u>who</u> had the foal is grey and white. _____

(f) The others horses <u>was</u> also in the stables. _____

3. Add describing words in the spaces to improve the sentences.

(a) I love to ride _____ horses.

(b) The _____ farmer cleaned out the stables.

(c) The horses galloped _____ around the field.

(d) They watched _____ as the horses galloped.

TEACHING WRITING STRATEGIES (Book 3)
www.prim-ed.com
978-1-912760-36-7

EDITED TEXT

Did you know jellyfish ~~isn't~~ *aren't* even fish at all? Even funnier, they don't have a brain! Some jellyfish can be large⊙ colourful and look like an umbrella⊙Others can be so small you can hardly see them. You can even see ~~write~~ *right* through some. Most are not harmful⊙/ *but,* Some are⊙They can have poison tentacles⊙Turtles, though, like *to* snack on some jellyfish?

> Good writers check their work carefully. They ask themselves: Is it right? How can I make it better?

Read the text carefully.

1. (a) How many full stops were added? _____

  (b) Find another missing full stop and add it.
     What is the word before this full stop?_____

2. (a) Find the comma the editor added. This comma is between the words

     _____ and _____.

  (b) Was this comma used in a list? _____

3. Which word was missing from the text? _____

4. (a) Find the verb the editor changed.

     It was changed from _____ to _____.

  (b) Why was it changed? _____

5. Why did the editor add the word 'but'?

     _____

     _____

6. Why was the word 'write' changed?

     _____

     _____

7. What is wrong with the punctuation mark at the end of the last sentence? Correct it.

     _____

UNIT 15

SPELLING (SUFFIXES), SENTENCE STRUCTURE, PUNCTUATION, WORD CHOICES, EDITING

Focus

Editing and proofreading – spelling (suffixes), sentence structure, punctuation, word choices, editing

Progression

Recognise

When editing and proofreading their writing, pupils will recognise correct and appropriate spelling, punctuation, word choices and sentence structure.

Choose

When editing and proofreading their writing, pupils will choose correct and appropriate spelling, punctuation, word choices and sentence structure.

Use

When editing and proofreading their writing, pupils will use correct and appropriate spelling, punctuation, word choices and sentence structure.

Definition of Terms

A **suffix** is a morpheme added at the end of a word to change the meaning or form.

Introduction

Good writers improve their writing by using correct spelling and punctuation and by choosing appropriate vocabulary, word choices and sentence structure.

Teacher Information

Knowledge of suffixes enables a writer to make informed choices in spelling.

LESSON NOTES AND PLANS

Introduction

• Discuss the purpose of editing and proofreading writing and how it is an essential part of the writing process.

Suffixes – Page 100

• Work with the class as a whole to revise/review the rules concerning suffix addition; for example, just add it; the one-one-one rule; when adding all, full, till, well or fill, drop one 'l'; no consonant doubled after a long vowel or double vowel; when adding 'ly' to words ending in 'e' after a consonant, just change 'e' to 'y' and so on. (Suggested reference: *Spelling Essentials* by Elizabeth Tucker—Prim-Ed Publishing PR-3002 ISBN 978-1-86400-523-3)

• List several examples on the board, working through them as a class.

• Read the information at the top of the page.

• Work as a class through Question 1(a).

• What word do they think is spelled incorrectly?

• What is the rule for adding the suffix?

• Correct the misspelled word.

• Work with those requiring additional assistance while the remainder of the class work independently on the activities.

Sentence Structure and Punctuation – Page 101

• Read the information at the top of the page.

• Revise common punctuation types with pupils; for example, full stops, commas and capital letters. Write them on the board.

• Emphasise that a sentence makes sense by itself.

• Read the text and work through Question 1 with pupils, providing support or additional information where needed.

• Continue to work with those requiring additional assistance while the remainder of the class work independently on the activities.

Word Choices – Page 102

• Read the information at the top of the page.

• Revise the importance of word choice when writing; for example, tenses, adverbs, adjectives, I or me, boring (pallid) verbs (got, said, went etc.).

• Allow pupils to work through the exercises, assisting as required.

Edited Text – Page 103

• Read the information at the top of the page. Emphasise the checking aspect.

• As a class, review the basic reasons for editing and proofreading; i.e. *to make it correct; to make it better.*

• Allow pupils time to read the text before commencing the activities.

• Discuss any problems that may arise at this time.

• Pupils work independently or with assistance on the activities.

UNIT 15 SPELLING (SUFFIXES), SENTENCE STRUCTURE, PUNCTUATION, WORD CHOICES, EDITING

ANSWERS

Suffixes – Page 100

1. (a) swimming
   (b) stopped
   (c) grabbed
   (d) travelled
   (e) quickest
   (f) winning
   (g) sitting
   (h) loudly
   (i) happily
   (j) proudly
   (k) taking
   (l) waving
   (m) hurried
   (n) writing
   (o) stories
   (p) chatted
   (q) carefully
   (r) clearly
   (s) weekly
   (t) properly
   (u) wanted
   (v) printed

Sentence Structure and Punctuation – Page 101

1. (a) Awesome!
   (b) Yes – They show the actual word spoken.
   (c) I could touch him, he's so friendly?

2. After 'awesome'.

3. It isn't needed because it is a statement.

4. Mum, Dad, Sam and I were at Sealand Park.

5. (a) we'd
   (b) 'we' and 'had'

6. (a) dolphins'
   (b) it's a possessive
   (c) didn't
   (d) 'did' and 'not'

Word Choices – Page 102

1. (a) came
   (b) come
   (c) come
   (d) finished
   (e) are
   (f) am
   (g) me
   (h) I
   (i) me
   (j) who
   (k) that
   (l) were
   (m) was

2.– 3. Teacher check

Edited Text – Page 103

1. (a) 'real'
   (b) Yes
   (c) No – capital 'R' for 'Roger'

2. (a) and
   (b)–(c) Teacher check

3. (a) weren't
   (b) It is a contraction.
   (c) Yes
   (d) wasn't

4. (a) wrong homophone
   (b) Yes

5. (a) crossbones, allowed
   (b) famos – famous

Assessment Activity – Page 112

1. (a) travelled
   (b) stopped
   (c) sitting
   (d) making
   (e) hurried
   (f) taking
   (g) carefully
   (h) greedily

2. (a) 3 full stops, 2 capital letters
   (b) lots
   (c) and they
   (d) yes

3. (a) came
   (b) me
   (c) who

4. Teacher check

Class Record Sheet – Page ix

ASSESSMENT WRITING

• **Paragraph Topic** – *Seals*

• **Focus: Punctuation – Editing and Proofreading** – *spelling (suffixes), sentence structure, punctuation, word choices, editing*

Self-evaluation – Page xiii

SUFFIXES

Good writers check that they have added suffixes correctly.

1. Underline the spelling mistake. Write the correct word on the line.

(a) Our class love going to swiming events at the pool. _____

(b) Yesterday, the bus stoped near the gate for us to board. _____

(c) We grabed our towels and climbed on. _____

(d) Then we traveled for ten minutes. _____

(e) My friend is one of the quickkest swimmers. _____

(f) She was wining her race easily. _____

(g) Her parents were siting in the stand and cheering. _____

(h) Everyone shouted loudely. _____

(i) They were happyly waiting for the result. _____

(j) She stood on the podium proudley. _____

(k) One of the girls was takeing her photo for the newsletter. _____

(l) In the stand I was waveing the school flag. _____

(m) After the races were over, we hurryed back to the bus. _____

(n) Back at school, the class had a writeing lesson. _____

(o) Then we had to write storyes about the swimming gala. _____

(p) In groups we chated about the exciting day. _____

(q) All the children tried to write carefuly. _____

(r) We needed to state our facts clearlly. _____

(s) The best ones will be chosen for the weeklly newsletter. _____

(t) They need to be properley edited. _____

(u) Everyone wantted their work to be selected. _____

(v) Our class can't wait to read the printted works. _____

SENTENCE STRUCTURE AND PUNCTUATION

> Good writers check their sentences make sense and that their punctuation is correct.

You will need a red pen or pencil to make corrections and changes to the text.

Mum Dad Sam and I were at Sealand Park. There were dolphins there doing tricks and leaping out of the water. One of the dolphins almost came out of the water and lay on the edge of the pool. 'Awesome!' gasped Sam 'I could touch him, he's so friendly?'

1. (a) What was written inside the first set of speech marks? _____

(b) Did this word need to have speech marks? _____

Why? _____

(c) What was written in the second set of speech marks?

_____

2. Find and circle the exclamation mark. _____

3. What is wrong with the question mark? _____

4. There are two missing commas. Add them and write the sentence.

_____

After we'd been at the dolphins' pool, we wandered off to watch the performing seals. They were so funny. They did some really clever tricks too. We didnt want to leave.

5. (a) Write the first word with an apostrophe. _____

(b) Which two words were joined to make this word? _____ and _____

6. (a) Write the second word with an apostrophe. _____

(b) Why does this word have an apostrophe?

_____

(c) Which word in the last sentence needs an apostrophe? _____

(d) The two words joined to make this word were _____ and

_____ .

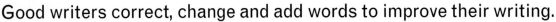

Good writers correct, change and add words to improve their writing.

1. Correct the underlined word. Write it on the line.

(a) Last weekend, our team <u>come</u> to play football. _____

(b) Lots of friends had <u>came</u> to watch the match. _____

(c) My family had to <u>came</u> along later. _____

(d) After the match had <u>finish</u>, the team went for a picnic. _____

(e) They <u>is</u> going to enjoy themselves. _____

(f) I <u>are</u> getting excited about it. _____

(g) My brother gave <u>I</u> a new football for my birthday. _____

(h) My friend and <u>me</u> will play with it. _____

(i) My brother will play with my friend and <u>I</u>. _____

(j) My brother <u>that</u> gave me the football is older than I am. _____

(k) The football <u>who</u> he gave me is brand new. _____

(l) We <u>was</u> having lots of fun playing with it. _____

(m) It <u>were</u> a great game. _____

2. Choose a better word. Write it on the line.

(a) 'Kick it to me', <u>said</u> my friend. _____

(b) 'Ouch, I've hurt my knee!' <u>said</u> my brother. _____

(c) 'Run and get help!' I <u>said</u> to my friend. _____

3. Add words in spaces to improve the sentences.

(a) We watched a _____ game of football.

(b) The _____ team were winning.

(c) One of the players kicked the ball _____.

(d) The ball landed _____ on the pitch.

Were pirates real. Yes, they were. They weren't like you see in films or read in stories. They sailed with a sku~~ll and cros~~ *crossbones* bones on their flag. This was called the 'Jolly roger'. It was'nt jolly to those who saw it! Women were~~n't~~ *allowed* aloud on ~~ships~~ *Two*. Too of them dressed up as men and became famos pirates.

> Good writers check their work carefully. They ask themselves: Is it right? How can I make it better?

Read the text carefully.

1. (a) Which word should have a question mark after it? _____

(b) Are there any proper nouns? _____

(c) Do they have the right punctuation? _____ Correct it.

2. (a) Which word was used to join two ideas in the last sentence? _____

(b) Write a sentence using this word.

_____

_____

(c) Does this word join two ideas in your sentence? _____

3. (a) Write the first word with an apostrophe. _____

(b) Why does it need an apostrophe? _____

(c) Is the apostrophe in the correct place? _____

(d) Write the second word with an apostrophe correctly. _____

4. (a) Why did the editor change the word 'too'? _____

(b) Is the other 'to' word in the text correct? _____

5. (a) Which two spelling mistakes did the editor correct?

_____ and _____

(b) Correct the spelling mistake the editor missed. _____

UNIT 16   SPELLING (HOMOPHONES), SENTENCE STRUCTURE, PUNCTUATION, WORD CHOICES, EDITING

Focus

Editing and proofreading – spelling, (homophones), sentence structure, punctuation, word choices, editing

Progression

Recognise
When editing and proofreading their writing, pupils will recognise correct and appropriate spelling, punctuation, word choices and sentence structure.

Choose
When editing and proofreading their writing, pupils will choose correct and appropriate spelling, punctuation, word choices and sentence structure.

Use
When editing and proofreading their writing, pupils will use correct and appropriate spelling, punctuation, word choices and sentence structure.

Definition of Terms

A **homophone** is a word that is pronounced the same as another word but which has a different meaning.

Introduction

Good writers improve their writing by using correct spelling and punctuation and by choosing appropriate vocabulary, word choices and sentence structure.

Teacher Information

Knowledge of homophones enables a writer to make more informed choices in spelling.

Introduction

- Discuss the purpose of editing and proofreading writing and how it is an essential part of the writing process.

Homophones – Page 106

- Work with the class as a whole to revise/review common homophones.
- List several examples on the board, working through them as a class.
- In pairs, pupils compete to see who can think of the longest list of homophones.
- Discuss the results as a class.
- Read the information at the top of the page.
- Read the instructions for Question 1. Emphasise that not every sentence will be incorrect.
- Work with those requiring additional assistance while the remainder of the class work independently on the activities.

Sentence Structure and Punctuation – Page 107

- Read the information at the top of the page.
- Revise common punctuation types with pupils; for example, full stops, commas and capital letters. Write them on the board.
- Emphasise that a sentence makes sense by itself.
- Read the text and work through Question 1 with pupils, providing support or additional information where needed.
- Continue to work with those requiring additional assistance while the remainder of the class work independently on the activities.

Word Choices – Page 108

- Read the information at the top of the page.
- Revise the importance of word choice when writing; for example, tenses, adverbs, adjectives, I or me, boring (pallid) verbs (got, said, went etc.).
- Allow pupils to work through the exercises, assisting as required.

Edited Text – Page 109

- Read the information at the top of the page. Emphasise the checking aspect.
- As a class, review the basic reasons for editing and proofreading; i.e. *to make it correct; to make it better.*
- Allow pupils time to read the text before commencing the activities.
- Discuss any problems that may arise at this time.
- Pupils work independently or with assistance on the activities.

UNIT 16 SPELLING (HOMOPHONES), SENTENCE STRUCTURE, PUNCTUATION, WORD CHOICES, EDITING

ANSWERS

Homophones – Page 106

1. (a) weak – week
   (b) correct
   (c) principle – principal
   (d) peace – piece
   (e) threw – through
   (f) bored – board
   (g) guest – guessed
   (h) weather– whether
   (i) correct
   (j) their – there
   (k) write – right
   (l) correct
   (m) scene – seen
   (n) correct

2. After the show, they're going to take their paintings and store them over there.

Sentence Structure and Punctuation – Page 107

1. (a) Teacher check – after 'flesh'
   (b) It is not a question.

2. (a) Apostrophe in the wrong place – They're
   (b) 'do' and 'not'
   (c) 'have' and 'not'

3. (a) No, not until extra full stop removed after 'flesh'.
   (b) They all start with 'they'.
   (c) Teacher check: Possible answer: They haven't even all got teeth, so they eat tiny creatures floating in the ocean.

Word Choices – Page 108

1. (a) were
   (b) was
   (c) am
   (d) collect
   (e) go
   (f) buy
   (g) It's
   (h) its
   (i) have
   (j) have

2. (a) seen
   (b) saw
   (c) see
   (d) that
   (e) who
   (f) are

3. Teacher check

Edited Text – Page 109

1. (a) Japan
   (b) 'In' – before Japan
   (c) you

2. (a) and
   (b) It

3. sandwich

4. (a) Teacher check. Possible answer: We might not eat it in sandwiches, but seaweed is really good for you.
   (b) but (Teacher check)

5. (a) Teacher check
   (b) Yes, it makes the text more informative and interesting.
   (c) Teacher check

6. (a) are
   (b) is

7. types

Assessment Activity – Page 113

1. (a) Too –Two
   (b) There – They're
   (c) weather – whether
   (d) guest – guessed
   (e) aloud – allowed

2. (a) popular and paintings
   (b) Yes, Woodvale School
   (c) 4
   (d) Teacher check. Possible answer:
       I've chosen two pieces for the show and they are seascapes.
   (e) Yes
   (f) I have

3. (a) who
   (b) were
   (c) are
   (d) come
   (e) It's

Class Record Sheet – Page ix

ASSESSMENT WRITING

- **Paragraph Topic** – *The Perfect Sandwich*
- **Focus: Editing and Proofreading** – *spelling (homophones), sentence structure, punctuation, word choices, editing*

Self-evaluation– Page xiii

HOMOPHONES

> Homophones are words that sound the same, but are written differently. Good writers check that they have written the correct homophone.

1. **Read the sentence. If an incorrect homophone has been used, put a line through it and write the correct one above it.**

   (a) Every year, our school holds an art show that lasts for a weak.

   (b) We are each allowed to exhibit one painting.

   (c) Our principle helps us to choose which one.

   (d) The peace I wanted to show was a seascape.

   (e) It showed a dolphin swimming threw the waves.

   (f) The seascape was painted on a wooden bored.

   (g) I guest the teacher liked it too.

   (h) She asked weather it was my favourite.

   (i) 'Where will you hang it?' I queried.

   (j) 'I think the piece will look better over their', replied the teacher.

   (k) 'It's important for it to look write', added my friend.

   (l) The main works were placed in the centre of the hall.

   (m) They could be more easily scene by everyone who visited the show.

   (n) I am sure we will receive lots of compliments.

2. **Read the sentence. Correct the homophones where needed. Rewrite the sentence.**

   After the show, there going to take they're paintings and store them over their.

   _____

   _____

   _____

SENTENCE STRUCTURE AND PUNCTUATION

Good writers check their sentences make sense and that their punctuation is correct.

You will need a red pen or pencil to make corrections and changes to the text.

Whales are the biggest animals in the sea or on the land. Theyr'e enormous. These creatures are mostly harmless? They don't need to rip flesh. from their prey. They haven't even all got teeth. They eat tiny creatures floating in the ocean.

1. (a) Did you notice there was an extra full stop? If not, find it now and cross it out.

(b) What is wrong with the question mark? Correct it.

_____

2. Find the three words with apostrophes and underline them.

(a) What is wrong with the first one? Correct the error.

_____

(b) Which two words were joined to make the second?

_____ and _____

(c) The third apostrophe is used in a word that is a contraction of _____ and 'not'.

3. Check the sentences.

(a) Do they all make sense? _____

(b) What is the problem with the last three sentences?

_____

(c) Join two of these sentences. Write your new sentence.

_____

_____

_____

_____

WORD CHOICES

Good writers correct, change and add words to improve their writing.

1. Correct the underlined word. Write it on the line.

(a) The girls <u>was</u> going to the theatre. _____

(b) The play <u>were</u> about animals. _____

(c) I wonder if I <u>were</u> going to enjoy it. _____

(d) Our teacher will <u>collects</u> the money for the tickets. _____

(e) We <u>goes</u> to the theatre every month. _____

(f) When will you <u>bought</u> your ticket? _____

(g) <u>Its</u> been on for quite a long time. _____

(h) The theatre has many posters about <u>it's</u> play. _____

(i) The girls could <u>of</u> been to see it sooner. _____

(j) They would <u>of</u> told me all about it. _____

2. Choose a better word. Write it on the line.

(a) We have <u>saw</u> many different plays. _____

(b) I <u>seen</u> my favourite play last month. _____

(c) Have you been to <u>saw</u> many plays? _____

(d) The play <u>who</u> is the best will win an award. _____

(e) The actors <u>that</u> are in the play are all very good. _____

(f) Lots of them <u>is</u> famous. _____

3. Add words in the spaces to improve the sentences.

(a) At the theatre, I watched a _____ play.

(b) We liked the _____ character the best.

(c) The audience applauded _____ at the finish.

(d) The cast smiled _____ from the stage.

How about a fat, juicy seaweed ~~sandwhich~~ *sandwich*? Sound yummy?

We might not eat it in sandwiches. Seaweed is really good for You.Not all seaweed of course, just certain type's. in japan, *cap* seaweed are more properly called a 'sea *and* vegetable'. It is a main ingredient in sushi.

> Good writers check their work carefully themselves: Is it right? How can I make it better?

Read the text carefully.

1. (a) Which proper noun did the editor correct? _____

   (b) Which other word in the text needs a capital letter? _____ Change it.

   (c) Which word has a capital letter it doesn't need?_____ Cross it out.

2. (a) Which conjunction did the editor use to join the last

   two sentences? _____

   (b) Which word needed to be crossed out? _____

3. Which spelling mistake did the editor find? _____

4. (a) Join Sentences 3 and 4. Write the new sentence.

   _____

   _____

   (b) What was the conjunction you used to join the sentences? _____

5. (a) Add another adjective to 'seaweed' in the first sentence. _____

   (b) Do you think this makes the text better? _____ Explain why you

   think this. _____

   (c) What is a different adjective you could have also added? _____

6. (a) Which verb is incorrect? _____

   (b) What should it be? _____ Change it.

7. Which word has an apostrophe it doesn't need? _____

Name: _____ Date: _____

1. Underline the word spelled incorrectly. Write it correctly on the line.

(a) I always go strate home after school. _____

(b) The team was so happie when it won the game. _____

(c) The eagle soared hie over the mountain. _____

(d) The hikers walked threw the dense jungle. _____

(e) The old bridge was built owver the river. _____

2. Join the two sentences. You will need to change the punctuation.

• We climbed out of the pool.   • We were cold.

_____

3. Add the missing punctuation.

our family travelled to green island by boat it was a long trip but we had fun On the way back, we saw dolphins.

4. Underline the incorrect word. Write it correctly on the line.

(a) The children done their work neatly. _____

(b) We have all did our best printing. _____

5. Choose a better word and write it on the line.

(a) Jack <u>got</u> a new ball for his birthday. _____

(b) Tom went to Jack's party and <u>Tom</u> enjoyed himself. _____

6. Add an adjective to tell more about the noun.

The _____ dog chased after the man.

7. Tell *how* the verb happened.

The shark swam _____ in the cool ocean.

8. Tell *where* the verb happened.

The man walked _____ and met his friend.

SPELLING (MORE VOWEL SOUNDS), SENTENCE STRUCTURE, PUNCTUATION, WORD CHOICES, EDITING

Name: _____ Date: _____

1. Underline the word spelled incorrectly. Write it correctly on the line.

(a) What jobs do you do to urn pocket money? _____

(b) Some people like to live in the cuontry. _____

(c) Can you rite neatly with your right hand? _____

(d) The hiker climed into the cave. _____

2. Underline the two words spelled incorrectly. Rewrite the sentence.

(a) The books were packed into large boxs by the classs.

_____

(b) I love to eat potatos and tomatos.

_____

3. Add describing words in the spaces to improve the sentence.

The _____ dolphin splashed _____ in the waves.

4. Correct the underlined word. Write it on the line.

(a) We <u>seen</u> lots of fish at the aquarium. _____

(b) The seahorse was looking after <u>it's</u> babies. _____

5. Read the text carefully.
Do you like to visit farms wev'e been to many we enjoy seeing the animals'. we especially enjoy the horses.

(a) What punctuation is missing from the end of sentences?

_____   _____

(b) Would Sentence 1, 2 or 3 be best as the first sentence?

(c) Does the word 'animals' need an apostrophe? _____

(d) Is the other apostrophe in the correct place? _____

(e) Join the last two sentences. _____

_____

SPELLING (SUFFIXES), SENTENCE STRUCTURE, PUNCTUATION, WORD CHOICES, EDITING

Name: _____ Date: _____

1. Underline the incorrect word and write it correctly on the line.

(a) Our class traveled on the bus to the pool. _____

(b) We stoped by the main entrance. _____

(c) Everyone was siting waiting for the swimming teachers. _____

(d) I have been makeing cakes for my lunch. _____

(e) Later, I hurryd to put them into the oven. _____

(f) I will enjoy takeing them to school. _____

(g) The cakes were placed carefuly in my schoolbag. _____

(h) My friends looked at them greedyly. _____

2. Mark any punctuation errors and answer the questions.

Every year, we hold a swimming gala lot's of children enter the races the parents come to watch us swim. The parents cheer loudly

(a) What punctuation did you add? I added ____ full stops and ____ capital letters.

(b) Correct the word that has an apostrophe in the wrong place. _____

(c) Add two words to join Sentences 3 and 4. _____

(d) Did you need to change any words? _____

3. Underline the incorrect word and write it correctly on the line.

(a) Lots of people come to see the gala last year. _____

(b) Who will come with Sally and I? _____

(c) The teacher that organised the gala was very busy. _____

4. Choose a better word. Write it on the line.

(a) 'Which swimming stroke do you like?' <u>said</u> the parent. _____

(b) 'We enjoy trying them all', <u>said</u> the children. _____

SPELLING (HOMOPHONES), SENTENCE STRUCTURE, PUNCTUATION, WORD CHOICES, EDITING

Name: _____ Date: _____

1. Write the correct homophone on the line.

    (a) <u>Too</u> of my paintings are in the show. _____

    (b) <u>There</u> going to be displayed in the hall. _____

    (c) I don't know <u>weather</u> my brother will come. _____

    (d) My mum <u>guest</u> which painting was mine. _____

    (e) Our class were <u>aloud</u> to see the art show first. _____

    Mark any punctuation errors and answer the questions.

    The art show at woodvale school is very popular many children show their paintings Iv'e chosen two pieces for the show. the pieces are seascapes.

2. (a) Write the words you needed to put a full stop after. _____

      and _____

    (b) Are there any proper nouns? _____

      Write them with capital letters. _____

    (c) How many complete sentences are there? _____

    (d) Join Sentences 3 and 4. _____

      _____

    (e) Look at the contraction. Is the apostrophe in the correct place? _____

    (f) Which two words have been shortened to make it? _____

3. Underline the incorrect word and write it correctly on the line.

    (a) The girl that painted the best picture won a prize. _____

    (b) We was looking forward to seeing the show. _____

    (c) All the children is choosing a picture. _____

    (d) Have you came before? _____

    (e) Its going to be a great night. _____